Bond

Verbal Reasoning

Assessment Papers

9–10 years
Book 2

Malcolm Thomas

Published in 2007 by:
Nelson Thornes Ltd
Delta Place
27 Bath Road
CHELTENHAM
GL53 7TH
United Kingdom

10 11 / 10 9 8 7 6 5 4

A catalogue record for this book is available from the British Library

ISBN 978 0 7487 8469 1

Page make-up by Tech Set Ltd

Printed and bound in Egypt by Sahara Printing Company

Before you get started

What is Bond?

This book is part of the Bond Assessment Papers series for verbal reasoning, which provides a **thorough and progressive course in verbal reasoning** from ages six to twelve. It builds up reasoning skills from book to book over the course of the series.

What does this book cover and how can it be used to prepare for exams?

Verbal reasoning questions can be grouped into four distinct groups: sorting words, selecting words, anagrams, coded sequences and logic. *Verbal Reasoning 9-10 Book 1* and *Book 2* practise a wide range of questions appropriate to the age group drawn from all these categories. The papers can be used both for general practice and as part of the run up to 11+ and other selective exams. One of the key features of Bond Assessment Papers is that each one practises **a very wide variety of skills and question types** so that children are always challenged to think – and don't get bored repeating the same question type again and again. We believe that variety is the key to effective learning. It helps children 'think on their feet' and cope with the unexpected: it is surprising how often children come out of verbal reasoning exams having met question types they have not seen before.

What does the book contain?

- **15 papers** – each one contains 65 questions.
- **Tutorial links throughout** - – this icon appears in the margin next to the questions. It indicates links to the relevant section in *How to do ... 11+ Verbal Reasoning*, our invaluable subject guide that offers explanations and practice for all core question types.
- **Scoring devices** – there are score boxes in the margins and a Progress Chart on page 60. The chart is a visual and motivating way for children to see how they are doing. It also turns the score into a percentage that can help decide what to do next.
- **Next Steps Planner** – advice on what to do after finishing the papers can be found on the inside back cover.
- **Answers** – located in an easily removed central pull-out section. If you lose your answers, please email cservices@nelsonthornes.com for another copy.

How can you use this book?

One of the great strengths of Bond Assessment Papers is their flexibility. They can be used at home, in school and by tutors to:

- set **timed formal practice** tests – allow about 40 minutes per paper. Reduce the suggested time limit by five minutes to practise working at speed.
- provide **bite-sized chunks** for regular practice
- **highlight strengths and weaknesses** in the core skills
- identify **individual needs**
- set **homework**
- follow a complete 11+ preparation strategy alongside *The Parents' Guide to the 11+* (see overleaf).

It is best to start at the beginning and work though the papers in order. If you are using the book as part of a careful run-in to the 11+, we suggest that you also have two other essential Bond resources close at hand:

How to do ... 11+ Verbal Reasoning: the subject guide that explains all the question types practised in this book. Use the cross-reference icons to find the relevant sections.

The Parents' Guide to the 11+: the step-by-step guide to the whole 11+ experience. It clearly explains the 11+ process, provides guidance on how to assess children, helps you to set complete action plans for practice and explains how you can use *Verbal Reasoning 9-10 Book 1* and *Book 2* as part of a strategic run-in to the exam.

See the inside front cover for more details of these books.

What does a score mean and how can it be improved?

It is unfortunately impossible to predict how a child will perform when it comes to the 11+ (or similar) exam if they achieve a certain score on any practice book or paper. Success on the day depends on a host of factors, including the scores of the other children sitting the test. However, we can give some guidance on what a score indicates and how to improve it.

If children colour in the Progress Chart on page 60, this will give an idea of present performance in percentage terms. The Next Steps Planner inside the back cover will help you to decide what to do next to help a child progress. It is always valuable to go over wrong answers with children. If they are having trouble with any particular question type, follow the tutorial links to *How to do ... 11+ Verbal Reasoning* for step-by-step explanations and further practice.

Don't forget the website...!

Visit www.bond11plus.co.uk for lots of advice, information and suggestions on everything to do with Bond, the 11+ and helping children to do their best.

Paper 1

Underline the pair of words most similar in meaning. B 5

Example come, go roam, wander fear, fare

1 test, exam learn, read science, mathematics

2 melt, fade dirty, clean rot, decay

3 drink, water eat, consume join, attract

4 hard, rough black, red light, pale

5 extend, enlarge side, back easy, late

Underline the two words, one from each group, which are the most opposite in meaning. B 9

Example (dawn, early, wake) (late, stop, sunrise)

6 (once, then, here) (never, open, now)

7 (large, hairy, wild) (tiny, untidy, cold)

8 (stretch, easy, loose) (pull, tight, take)

9 (awake, dark, hollow) (solid, open, confused)

10 (second, minute, first) (hour, third, final) 5

Complete the following sentences by selecting the most sensible word from each group of words given in the brackets. Underline the words selected. B 14

Example The (children, books, foxes) carried the (houses, books, steps) home from the (greengrocer, library, factory).

11 The (farmer, teacher, shopkeeper) asked the (men, sheep, children) to eat their (shoes, lunches, flowers) sensibly.

12 Don't (try, remember, forget) (swimming, jumping, running) in such a strong (puddle, tide, night).

13 Why are those (boats, trees, cows) standing (huddled, wide, near) together in the (shop, ground, field)?

14 The (team, colour, home) scored a (peach, ball, goal) to win the (last, match, run).

15 James (rubbed, used, whisked) the (jumper, dessert, pencil) with a (hose, pound, fork). 5

B 7

Underline the two words which are made from the same letters.

Example TAP PET TEA POT EAT

16	SHADES	SHADOW	SHIELD	DASHES	SHINES
17	STARS	TEARS	STATE	TEASE	RATES
18	PEARS	STEER	SPEAR	PLEAT	TREAT
19	SHOVE	FLASH	FLESH	SHAVE	SHELF
20	LATER	STEEL	TRAIL	STEAL	LEAST

Find the four-letter word hidden at the end of one word and the beginning of the next word. The order of the letters may not be changed.

Example The children had bats and balls. sand

21 He decided to have breakfast early that morning. ______

22 The garage mechanic repaired her new car promptly. ______

23 'Don't I get a hello any more?' asked Mum. ______

24 He put a larger dynamo onto the old bicycle. ______

25 This was a radical move for Professor Furey. ______

B 10

Find the letter which will end the first word and start the second word.

Example peac (h) ome

26 mal (___) scape

27 pou (___) eat

28 see (___) ade

29 tea (___) ota

30 soa (___) ure

B 17

Find and underline the two words which need to change places for each sentence to make sense.

Example She went to letter the write.

31 The motor lake roared across the calm boat.

32 You thought that she couldn't hear I.

33 The mechanic was repaired by the car.

34 Where is you think she do going?

35 The caged sea roared like a angry lion.

5

Fill in the missing letters. The alphabet has been written out to help you. B 23

A B C D E F G H I J K L M N O P Q R S T U V W X Y Z

Example AB is to CD as PQ is to RS

36 JK is to LM as RS is to ______

37 GE is to DB as AY is to ______

38 EF is to HI as KL is to ______

39 T5 is to V7 as X9 is to ______

40 XX is to YA as BB is to ______

Which one letter can be added to the front of all of these words to make new words? B 12

Example care cat crate call

41 ___old ___read ___ait ___rand

42 ___and ___old ___oup ___hare

43 ___otion ___ay ___ould ___ore

44 ___our ___outh ___oung ___ell

45 ___live ___bate ___bout ___mend

Fill in the crosswords so that all the given words are included. You have been given one letter as a clue in each crossword.

46

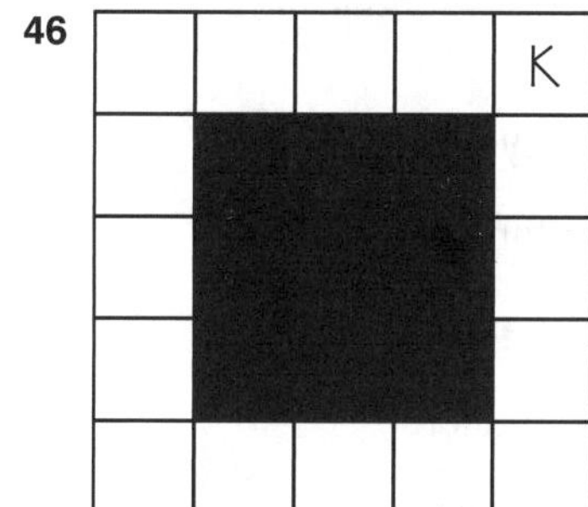

tiles, shark, start, knees

47

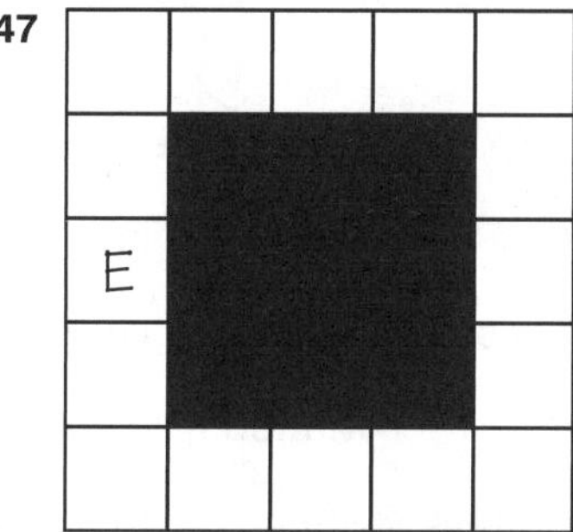

tries, fresh, front, heads

48

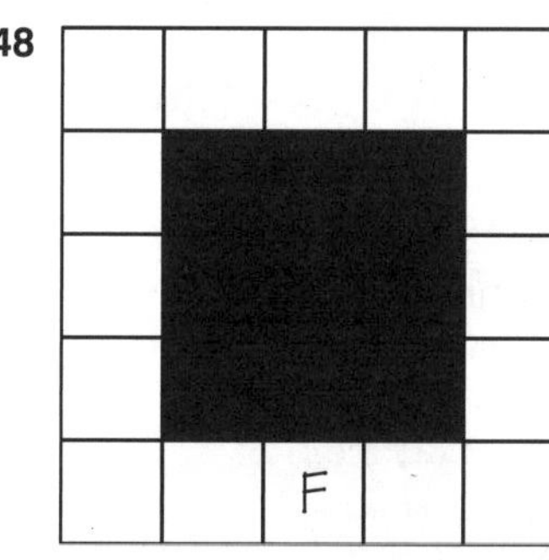

tufts, elves, aloft, above

49

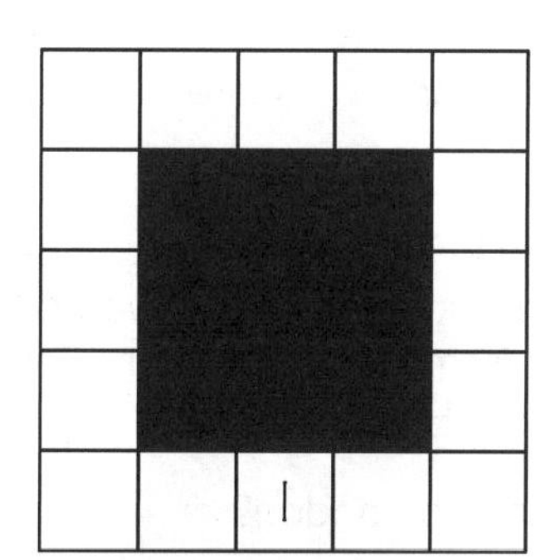

empty, round, rupee, daisy

50

		U		
	■	■	■	
	■	■	■	
	■	■	■	

grand, gruel, dough, laugh

5

If the code for TRAVEL is $ * : £ – &, what are the codes for the following words? B 24

51 REAL ____________

52 TEAR ____________

53 LEAVE ____________

If the code for TRAIN is @ < ? > !, what do these codes stand for?

54 @ ? < ____________

55 @ ? > ! @ ____________

5

Underline the one word which **cannot be made** from the letters of the word in capital letters. B 7

Example	STATIONERY	stone	tyres	ration	<u>nation</u>	noisy
56	DETAILED	late	dated	laid	leaded	tamed
57	SUPERVISE	revise	revue	vipers	every	serve
58	COMPLICATED	laced	matted	calmed	placed	malice
59	MANAGEMENT	games	agent	magenta	meant	game
60	TIDEMARK	taker	dream	dimmer	marked	armed
61	ESTRANGE	gears	snare	grates	earns	groan

6

A football match is being held in London. To get there, you would have to travel 12 km from Wiston. If you lived in Bridgeworth you would have to go 4 km further than from Wiston but 6 km less than from Hambury. From Fettle it is only half the distance to London that it would be from Hambury. B 25

62 Which town is closest to London? ____________

63 Which town is furthest from London? ____________

64 How far is Bridgeworth from London? ________

65 How much further from London is Wiston than Fettle? ________ 4

Now go to the Progress Chart to record your score! Total 65

Paper 2

Underline the two words in each line which are most similar in type or meaning. B 5

Example	dear	pleasant	poor	extravagant	expensive
1 withdraw	build	retrain	construct	demolish	
2 destroy	remove	put	place	lie	
3 attempt	adjust	leave	reveal	try	
4 starting	grave	thoughtful	ending	serious	
5 easy	correct	wrong	complex	effortless	5

Underline the pair of words most opposite in meaning. B 9

Example cup, mug	coffee, milk	hot, cold
6 flat, even	false, true	strange, wild
7 continuous, ended	allowed, admitted	flaky, dry
8 quick, swift	plain, elegant	hunch, guess
9 wet, damp	truth, honesty	criticise, praise
10 cured, improved	full, complete	well, ill	5

Underline the two words, one from each group, that go together to form a new word. The word in the first group always comes first. B 8

Example (hand, green, for) (light, house, sure)

11 (good, high, flat) (friend, out, mate)

12 (cold, wet, at) (put, tack, pie)

13 (for, try, down) (lawn, late, sake)

14 (on, out, way) (fold, cry, lie)

15 (left, in, far) (vest, way, out) 5

Find the three-letter word which can be added to the letters in capitals to make a new word. The new word will complete the sentence sensibly. B 22

Example The cat sprang onto the MO. USE

16–17 Jane's BHER told her that his cat had FOLED him to school that day. ______ ______

18–20 Her CLASSE told Seena she should TELEPH her mother to come and collect her IMMEDILY. ______ ______ ______

5

Find the four-letter word hidden at the end of one word and the beginning of the next word. The order of the letters may not be changed. B 21

Example The children had bats and balls. sand

21 He reached the deadline in time. ______

22 The rusty old door opened with a scary creak. ______

23 Tara reminded her mother that Monday was a holiday. ______

24 On Sunday the hen would stop laying eggs. ______

25 The prisoner shouted his plea several times. ______

5

Change the first word into the last word, by changing one letter at a time and making a new, different word in the middle. B 13

Example CASE CASH LASH

26 PUSH ______ POST

27 REAR ______ SEAT

28 LAST ______ HOST

29 FINE ______ MINT

30 STAR ______ SNAG

5

Complete the following sentences by selecting the most sensible word from each group of words given in the brackets. Underline the words selected. B 14

Example The (children, books, foxes) carried the (houses, books, steps) home from the (greengrocer, library, factory).

31 When will we (land, address, arrive) in our (fresh, artistic, holiday) (conservatory, resort, canvas)?

32 Which (way, man, frog) do we (eat, go, hunt) to get to the (theatre, lunch, flower)?

33 The (quiet, hungry, learner) driver kept (eating, speeding, stalling) the car's (supper, engine, wheels).

34 In the (hungry, spotted, haunted) (bush, castle, wagon) lived an evil (spirit, brick, bathroom).

35 In (art, mathematics, history) we learn about (dance, football, graphs) and (television, numbers, drawing).

Choose two words, one from each set of brackets, to complete the sentences in the best way.

Example Smile is to happiness as (drink, <u>tear</u>, shout) is to (whisper, laugh, <u>sorrow</u>).

36 Monday is to Wednesday as (Tuesday, Thursday, Sunday) is to (Monday, Wednesday, Saturday).

37 Flight is to aircraft as (walk, trial, sailing) is to (car, ship, automobile).

38 Rim is to plate as (picture, shore, water) is to (lake, painting, drink).

39 Uncertain is to sure as (tired, restricted, grateful) is to (late, unlimited, trained).

40 Trivial is to insignificant as (considerate, unstable, trembling) is to (generous, prudent, unkind).

5

Fill in the crosswords so that all the given words are included. You have been given one letter as a clue in each crossword.

41

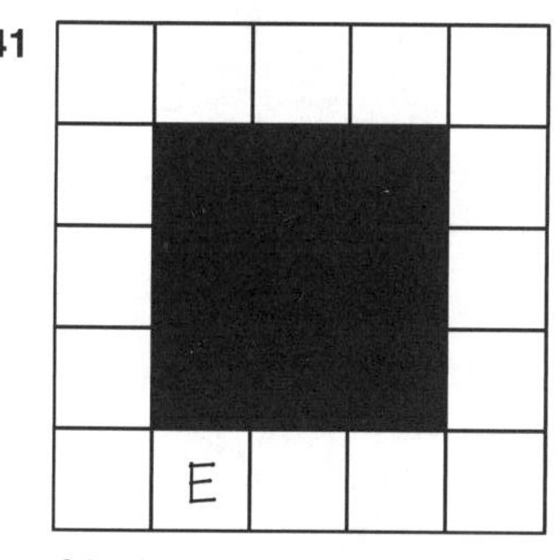

fried, hatch, death, fetch

42

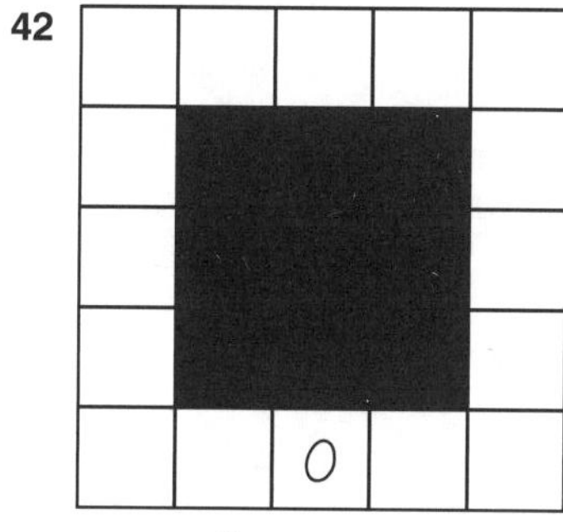

story, diary, grind, goats

43

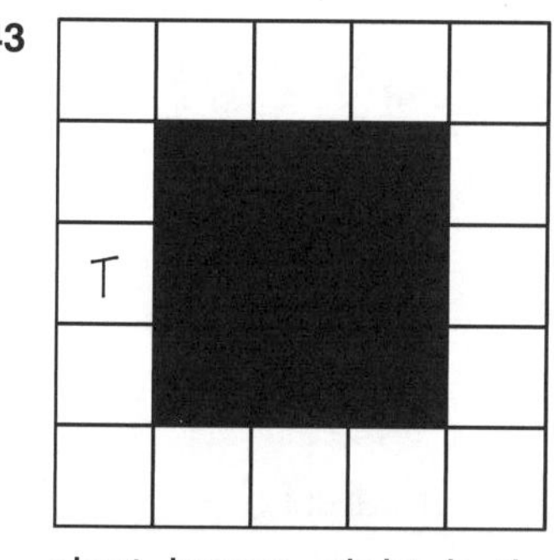

elect, brown, night, bathe

44

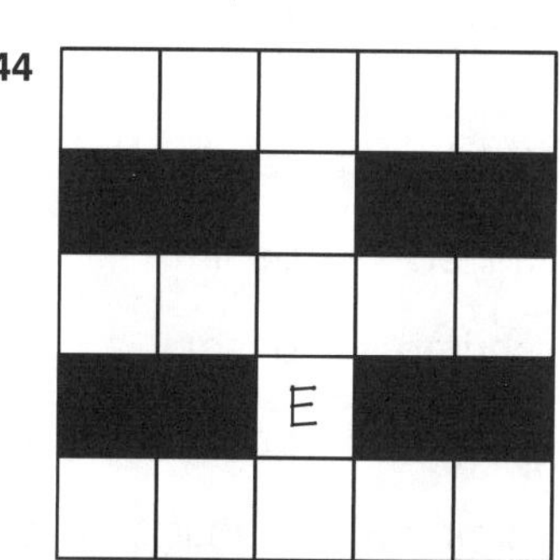

irate, after, forge, later

45

■	■		■	■
		E		
■	■		■	■

chest, metre, mocha, pleat

5

Give the missing numbers in the following sequences. B 23

Example 2 4 6 8 10 <u>12</u>

46	62	58	___	50	46	42
47	6	7	9	12	16	___
48	1	5	3	___	5	9
49	15	25	20	30	___	35
50	1	2	4	8	___	32

5

If the code for BALLISTIC is < > ? ? £ % X £ +, what are the codes for the following words? B 24

51 BALLS ______

52 LIST ______

53 STAB ______

What do these codes stand for?

54 £ ? ? ______

55 + > ? ? ______

5

Underline the one word in each group which **cannot be made** from the letters of the word in capital letters. B 7

Example STATIONERY stone tyres ration <u>nation</u> noisy

56	REMAINDER	mined	denim	rider	married	drained
57	WORKMANSHIP	shrimp	prism	hawks	plank	sharp
58	TELEVISION	version	invites	seven	event	list
59	ARRANGEMENT	remnant	manager	anger	garment	nearest
60	PERSONAL	snare	polar	salon	plain	loans

5

Anna supports France and England. Liam supports Wales and England. Malik does not support Scotland but supports Wales. Donna supports Scotland, England and Brazil. David hates football.

B 25

61 How many teams do Donna and Malik support together? ________

62 Which country has the most supporters? ________

2

Eleanor lives 5 km from school. Michael lives nearest to school. Francesca lives 2 km closer than Eleanor, who lives 4 km further from the school than Michael. Robert lives 1 km further than Michael.

B 25

63 Who lives furthest from school? ________

64 How much nearer to school is Michael than Francesca? ________

2

Charlotte is five years older than Lianne, who is four years younger than Lily. Lily is one year older than Ellie, who is three years older than Jessica. Ellie is 10.

B 25

65 Which two girls are twins? ________________

1

Now go to the Progress Chart to record your score! Total 65

Paper 3

Underline the word in the brackets closest in meaning to the words in capitals.

B 5

Example	UNHAPPY	(unkind death laughter <u>sad</u> friendly)
1	PULL, TUG	(drop drag eat kick boat)
2	WASP, BEETLE	(butterfly horse salmon snake mouse)
3	POMEGRANATE, TOMATO	(sprout lettuce apple onion beetroot)
4	CONTRACT, PACT	(agreement code shrink invitation signature)
5	WALES, FINLAND	(London Essex Leeds Russia Kent)

5

Underline the two words, one from each group, which are the most opposite in meaning.

B 9

Example	(dawn, <u>early</u>, wake)	(<u>late</u>, stop, sunrise)
6	(wonder, love, try)	(find, heat, hate)
7	(hard, fine, soft)	(furry, effortless, light)
8	(reject, refill, waste)	(conserve, rubbish, useful)
9	(fair, honest, closed)	(just, truthful, dark)
10	(reduce, infinite, counted)	(endless, hourly, limited)

5

Find the letter that will end the first word and start the second word. B 10

Example peac (h) ome

11 fus (__) dge

12 mat (__) lse

13 coa (__) imb

14 int (__) ath

15 shu (__) umb 5

Find a word that can be put in front of each of the following words to make new, compound words. B 11

Example	CAST	FALL	WARD	POUR	DOWN
16	KNOB	STEP	MAT	BELL	______
17	BY	STILL	POINT	PIPE	______
18	KEEPER	TABLE	SCALE	SHARE	______
19	PAPER	AGENT	REEL	FLASH	______
20	ACHE	BURN	BEAT	FELT	______

5

Find the four-letter word hidden at the end of one word and the beginning of the next word. The order of the letters may not be changed. B 21

Example The children had bats and balls. sand

21 She is at her wits' end with her homework. ______

22 Please empty your pockets before putting your trousers in the laundry. ______

23 The biscuits are at the back of the cupboard. ______

24 As it hurtled down the street, the car turned and spun round. ______

25 The fiercest of dinosaurs lived throughout the cretaceous age. ______ 5

Find and underline the two words which need to change places for each sentence to make sense. B 17

Example She went to letter the write.

26 Who have could dreamed that it would come true?

27 After computer I like to play on my school.

28 Two plus four is two.

29 It is never steal to right.

30 Where in the China is world? 5

Give the missing numbers in the following sequences. B 23

Example	2	4	6	8	10
31	15	12	9	6	___
32	11	33	___	77	99
33	128	64	32	___	8
34	5	8	12	17	___
35	54	45	36	___	18

5

Fill in the crosswords so that all the given words are included. You have been given one letter as a clue in each crossword. B 19

36

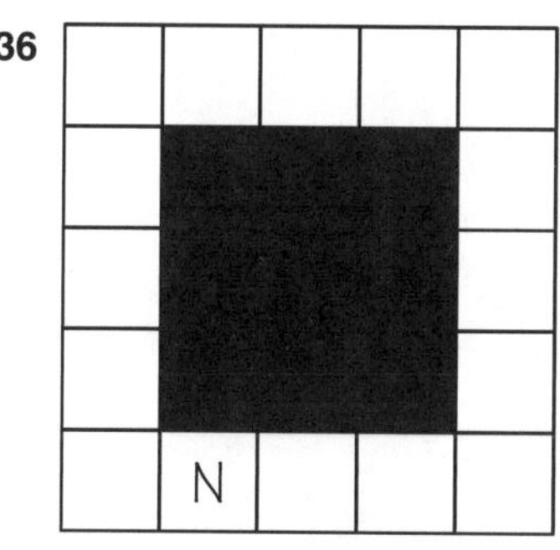

their, enter, paint, price

37

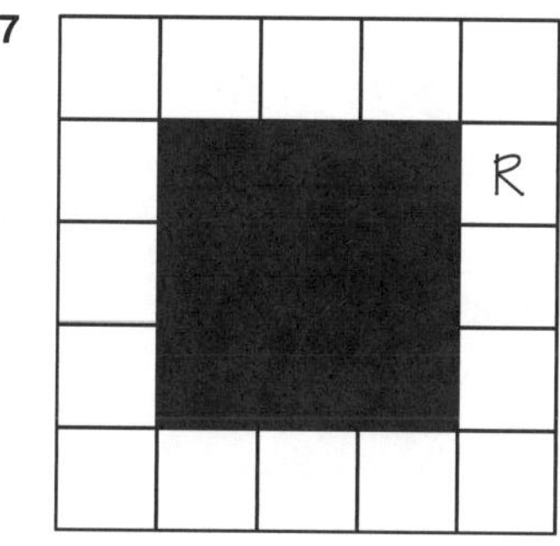

event, stand, shade, draft

38

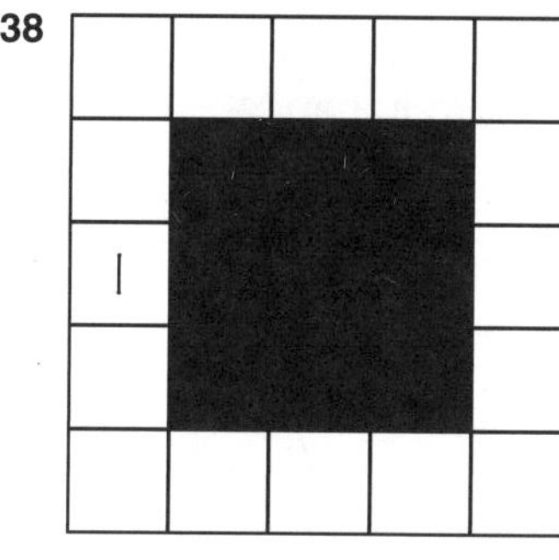

reign, thorn, faint, flair

39

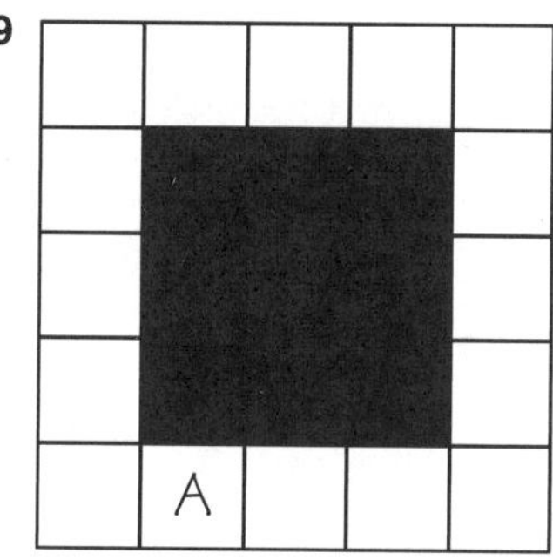

tardy, truth, taint, holly

40

magic, flown, attic, ghost

5

Choose two words, one from each set of brackets, to complete the sentences in the best way. B 15

Example Smile is to happiness as (drink, tear, shout) is to (whisper, laugh, sorrow).

41 First is to last as (late, second, aged) is to (fine, young, final).

42 Shirt is to cloth as (sock, shoe, earring) is to (string, grass, leather).

43 Past is to present as (once, lessen, increase) is to (multiply, last, first).

44 Halve is to double as (change, third, force) is to (remain, second, unravel).

45 Constant is to always as (final, unique, copied) is to (original, late, related). 5

If the code for C H A N G E A B L E is written ! ‘ £ $ % ^ £ & * ^, what are the codes for the following words? B 24

46 HANG __________

47 ABLE __________

What do these codes stand for?

48 & £ * * __________

49 & ^ £ $ __________

50 £ ! ‘ ^ __________ 5

Underline the one word which **cannot be made** from the letters of the word in capital letters. B 7

Example	STATIONERY	stone	tyres	ration	nation	noisy
51	PORCELAIN	plain	clear	price	race	relay
52	COMMERCIAL	cream	realm	alert	moral	rice
53	GRINDSTONE	tried	stored	noted	rested	nesting
54	INVESTIGATE	tease	sting	ingest	testing	starve
55	SIGNATURE	agent	ignore	rents	great	surge

5

In football Alison can play in goal or in defence. Soraya can play in midfield or in attack. James never plays in goal, but can play in other positions. Lena can play in midfield or in attack. Kim can play in any position. Geeta can play in defence or midfield. B 25

56 Who can play in any position except in goal? __________

57 Which two children play the same positions? __________

58 If Alison is ill, who will play in goal? __________

59 How many children can play in attack? ________

60 How many children can play in midfield but not defence? ________ 5

Rearrange the muddled letters in capitals to make a proper word. The answer will complete the sentence sensibly. B 16

Example A BEZAR is an animal with stripes. ZEBRA

61 We put one foot in front of the other when we LWKA. ________

62 NALIF is another word for last. ________

63 We are taught a SENLOS. ________

64 I have TPSNE all my pocket money. ________

65 REELTTS make up the alphabet. ________ 5

Now go to the Progress Chart to record your score! Total 65

Paper 4

Underline the two words, one from each group, which are closest in meaning. B 3

Example (race, shop, start) (finish, begin, end)

1 (push, trace, flash) (take, shove, fly)

2 (weed, creep, weep) (rush, cry, flip)

3 (spoil, try, mend) (ignore, waste, repair)

4 (refuse, control, retry) (manage, oppose, enjoy)

5 (uphold, agree, stay) (refuse, support, change) 5

Find the three-letter word which can be added to the letters in capitals to make a new word. The new word will complete the sentence sensibly. B 22

Example The cat sprang onto the MO. USE

6 We had chocolate PUDG for dessert. ________

7 It is a SE that it is raining, as we wanted to go out. ________

8 We had MALADE on our toast. ________

9 She decided to SPRLE marshmallows on her hot chocolate. ________

10 The store AGER asked the customers if she could help them. ________ 5

Find the letter that will end the first word and start the second word.

Example peac (h) ome

11 mas (___) nit

12 sal (___) ach

13 tin (___) ard

14 pri (___) ask

15 man (___) dit

B 10

5

Find a word that can be put in front of each of the following words to make new, compound words.

Example CAST FALL WARD POUR DOWN

16 DOORS	SIDE	LINE	FIT	______
17 WORKS	MONGER	CLAD	WARE	______
18 MAN	FLAKE	DROP	BALL	______
19 BALL	LASH	SHADOW	LID	______
20 MAN	CARD	CODE	BOX	______

B 11

5

Find the four-letter word hidden at the end of one word and the beginning of the next word. The order of the letters may not be changed.

Example The children had bats and balls. sand

21 Each inspector must be well trained. ______

22 The tired old man came along the street slowly. ______

23 The train the *Golden Pride* approached slowly along the track. ______

24 He had certainly made advances with his handwriting. ______

25 He applied for his library card because he liked reading. ______

B 21

5

Change the first word of the third pair in the same way as the other pairs to give a new word.

Example bind, hind bare, hare but, hut

26 pit, tip	rat, tar	tub, ______
27 made, mace	fade, face	ride, ______
28 part, start	pale, stale	peer, ______
29 seal, sale	meal, male	fear, ______
30 flea, leaf	stag, tags	plea, ______

B 18

5

Complete the following sentences by selecting the most sensible word from each group of words given in the brackets. Underline the words selected.

B 14

Example The (children, books, foxes) carried the (houses, books, steps) home from the (greengrocer, library, factory).

31 The fastest (girl, cheetah, car) in the (shop, school, forest) came (last, once, first) in the 100 metre race.

32 I wonder if we will be (calling, eating, taking) a spelling (cry, test, man) next (cake, week, word).

33 (Charging, Flying, Climbing) mountains can be (trusting, easy, dangerous) in poor (weather, hunger, air).

34 Daisy (felt, wondered, knew) whether she should (try, fall, rub) to call for (food, excellence, assistance).

35 (Always, Never, Forever) forget to (start, make, brush) your (feet, hands, teeth) before going to bed.

5

Find and underline the two words which need to change places for each sentence to make sense.

B 17

Example She went to letter the write.

36 Once upon a woman there lived an old time.

37 There been have two assemblies today.

38 The baby was crying the through all night.

39 This is the very last tell I am going to time you!

40 I wonder that he decided to do why.

5

Complete the following expressions by filling in the missing word.

B 15

Example Pen is to ink as brush is to paint

41 Three is to third as nine is to ________.

42 England is to English as France is to ________.

43 Month is to year as decade is to ________.

44 High is to low as up is to ________.

45 Land is to dry as sea is to ________.

5

Give the missing letters and numbers in the following sequences. The alphabet has been written out to help you.

B 23

A B C D E F G H I J K L M N O P Q R S T U V W X Y Z

Example CQ DQ EP FP GO HO

46 C F I L ___ ___

47 DC DD DE DF ___ ___

48 A3 B5 C7 ___ E11 ___

49 YB WD ___ SH QJ ___

50 ___ ___ RQ NM JI FE

5

Solve the problems by working out the letter codes. The alphabet has been written out to help you.

B 24

A B C D E F G H I J K L M N O P Q R S T U V W X Y Z

Example In a code SECOND is written as UGEQPF. How would you write THIRD? VJKTF

51 In a code PRINCE is written as NPGLAC. How would you write NICE? ___________

52 In a code ICON is written as HBNM. What does SVHF stand for? ___________

53 In a code APE is written as BRH. How would you write LOOK? ___________

54 In a code FEEL is written as IHHO. How would you write WAIT? ___________

55 In a code RICE is written as VMGI. How would you write DOG? ___________

5

Ann and Rhinffrew like lemonade. Peter likes cola, but not lemonade. Siobhan likes orange and cola. Angus only likes cola.

B 25

56 Which is the most popular drink? ___________

57 Which person likes the most types of drink? ___________

2

Chester is west of Birmingham, but east of Bangor. Shrewsbury is south of Chester.

B 25

58 Which town is furthest west? ___________

1

Three years ago Simeon was three years old. In four years' time he will be twice the age of his sister Sophie. Their mother is five times Simeon's age now. Their father is two years older than their mother.

B 25

59 How old will Sophie be in four years' time? ______

60 How old was their mother three years ago? ______

61 How old is their father now? ______

62 How much older is Simeon than Sophie? ______

4

If a = 1, b = 3, c = 4, d = 6, e = 10, find the answer to these calculations:

B 26

63 $e - d =$ ______

64 $d \div b =$ ______

65 $a + b + c =$ ______

3

Now go to the Progress Chart to record your score! Total 65

Paper 5

1–5 Look at these groups of words.

H	C	G
Homes	Containers	Games

Choose the correct group for each of the words below. Write in the letter.

skipping ___ basket ___ Cluedo ___ urn ___

den ___ flat ___ cup ___ lodge ___

casket ___ snakes and ladders ___

B 1 5

Find the three-letter word which can be added to the letters in capitals to make a new word. The new word will complete the sentence sensibly.

B 22

Example The cat sprang onto the MO. USE

6 CARS are my favourite vegetables. ________

7 The nurse put some OINTT on the wound. ________

8 The WING machine was full of dirty clothes. ________

9 The old lady DEDED on her carer to help her get out of bed. ________

10 The volcano was INIVE and no longer spewed out molten lava. ________ 5

Find the letter which will end the first word and start the second word.

B 10

Example peac (h) ome

11 fin (___) oze

12 mal (___) ive

13 poin (___) rip

14 kis (___) ite

15 me (___) age 5

Write the letters of each of the following words in alphabetical order, then circle the fifth letter in each word.

B 20

16 FAMILY ________

17 READING ________

18 LIGHTER ________

19 TUESDAY ________

20 BOUNCE ________ 5

Find the four-letter word hidden at the end of one word and the beginning of the next word. The order of the letters may not be changed. B 21

Example The children had bats and balls. <u>sand</u>

21 Sarah asked her brother to turn his music down. ________

22 The teacher announced that there appeared to be a problem with the computers. ________

23 The corporal ordered his troops to stand to attention. ________

24 'Please stop interrupting!' said the teacher. ________

25 The sofa remained in place by the door. ________

5

Add one letter to the word in capital letters to make a new word. The meaning of the new word is given in the clue. B 12

Example PLAN simple <u>plain</u>

26 EVER not at all ________

27 STRIP a band of colour ________

28 CHAP not expensive ________

29 THOUGH in one side and out the other ________

30 RESTED taken by force ________

5

Complete the following sentences by selecting the most sensible word from each group of words given in the brackets. Underline the words selected. B 14

Example The (<u>children</u>, books, foxes) carried the (houses, <u>books</u>, steps) home from the (greengrocer, <u>library</u>, factory).

31 (Two, three, four) times (three, four, five) makes (eight, eighteen, eighty).

32 The (force, black, strong) wind blew through the (broken, pattern, fast) window.

33 In which (shirt, shop, shape) can we buy (card, painted, chocolate) (clouds, swimmers, cakes)?

34 Who (was, would, wish) like to (eat, hide, try) on their new school (uniform, canteen, hall)?

35 We were (shot, ate, flew) at by an (untidy, uneaten, unseen) (lunch, army, bedroom).

5

Complete the following sentences in the best way by choosing one word from each set of brackets. B 15

Example Tall is to (tree, <u>short</u>, colour) as narrow is to (thin, white, <u>wide</u>).

36 Shout is to (whisper, scream, noisy) as loud is to (low, quiet, cosy).

37 Hat is to (face, head, coat) as mittens is to (cat, wool, hands).

38 Government is to (rule, elect, law) as school is to (teach, classroom, pupil).

39 Red is to (food, danger, colour) as centimetre is to (weight, green, measurement).

40 Grand is to (grown, impressive, lesson) as modest is to (reduced, proud, plain). 5

Fill in the crosswords so that all the given words are included. You have been given one letter as a clue in each crossword. B 19

41
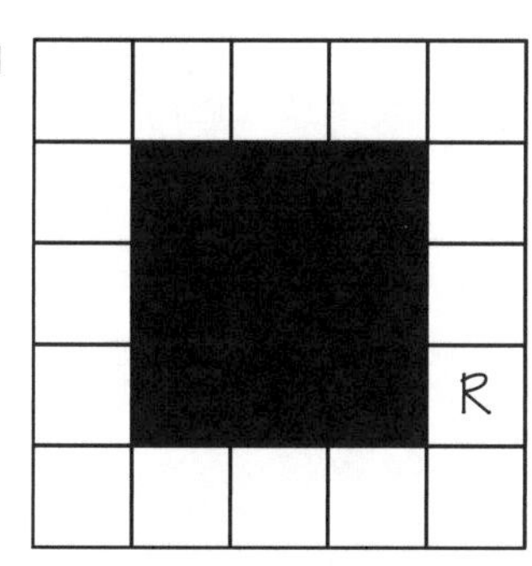

salad, daily, scale, entry

42
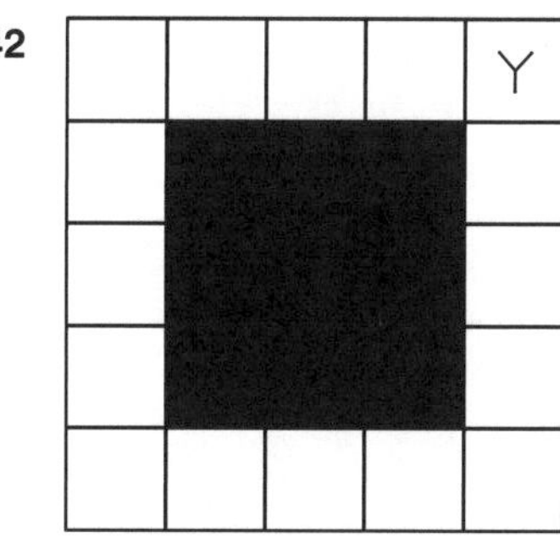

water, rings, yards, windy

43
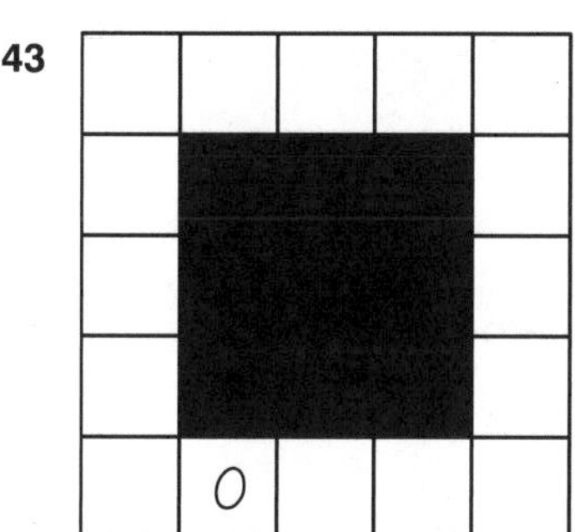

roads, elves, frame, fever

44
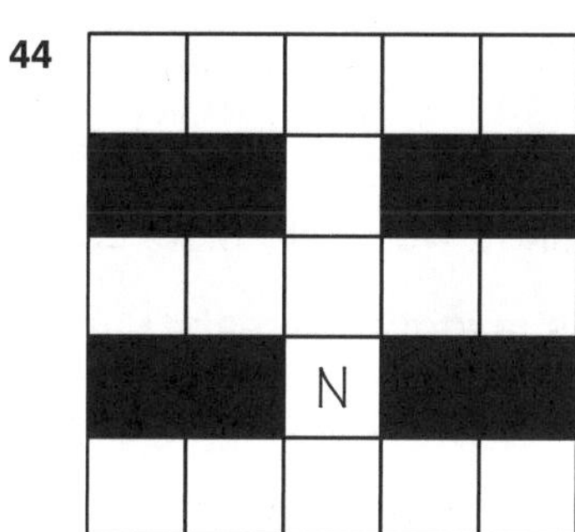

miser, sunny, funny, tryst

45

loves, caves, halls, misty

5

If the code for TRAVEL is USBWFM, what are the codes for the following words? B 24

46 LEVEL __________

47 LEAVE __________

48 EVER __________ 3

If the code for CUTE is DVUF, what do these codes stand for?

B 24

49 SBSF ________

50 MJTU ________

2

If a = 3, b = 5, c = 12, d = 15, e = 2, f = 10, give the answers to these calculations as letters.

B 26

51 d – f = ______

52 a + e = ______

53 b × a = ______

54 d ÷ a = ______

55 b × e = ______

5

Choose the word or phrase that makes each sentence true.

B 14

Example A LIBRARY always has (posters, a carpet, books, DVDs, stairs).

56 A DESK always has (glass, books, pens, legs, children).

57 A LAKE is always (sandy, wet, salty, blue, deep).

58 A TRUCK always has (a roof, four seats, passengers, petrol, carpet).

59 A COUNTRY always has (a king, a queen, a parliament, a border, a president).

60 GLASS is always (hard, transparent, clean, square, frosted).

5

B 25

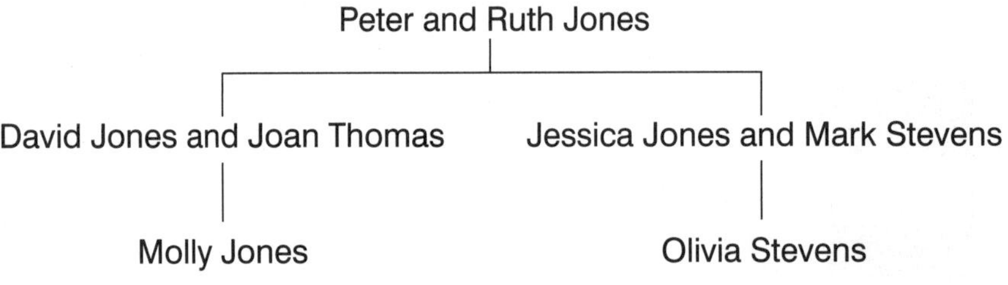

61 Peter is David's (brother, uncle, father, grandfather).

62 Jessica is Ruth's (sister, aunt, mother, daughter).

63 Molly is Ruth's (daughter, sister, mother, granddaughter).

64 Olivia is David's (daughter, niece, mother, sister).

65 Peter is Mark's (father, brother, grandfather, father-in-law).

5

Now go to the Progress Chart to record your score! Total 65

Paper 6

Underline the pair of words most similar in meaning. B 5

Example come, go roams, wanders fear, fare

1 awake, asleep gift, present sweet, bitter

2 top, peak warm, cool hole, hill

3 big, small question, answer follow, pursue

4 please, delight create, destroy fall, rise

5 failure, victory judgement, decision allow, refuse 5

Find the three-letter word which can be added to the letters in capitals to make a new word. The new word will complete the sentence sensibly. B 22

Example The cat sprang onto the MO. USE

6 He found it difficult to SK as his mouth was so dry. ____

7 You must MULLY three by three to get 9. ____

8 SE birthday is it today? ____

9 She found the question difficult to UNDERSD. ____

10 The sisters had a DISAGREET over who should get the bed near the window. ____ 5

Find the letter which will end the first word and start the second word. B 10

Example peac (h) ome

11 fligh (__) rip

12 pra (__) onder

13 flak (__) nd

14 ris (__) ite

15 bea (__) rial 5

Rearrange the muddled letters in capitals to make a proper word. The answer will complete the sentence sensibly. B 16

Example A BEZAR is an animal with stripes. ZEBRA

16 The time is now a ATEQRRU past five. ____

17 He had VESRREED the car into the parking space. ____

18 I like to have some RVYAG on my mashed potatoes. ______

19 The manager named the SRELPAY for the next match. ______

20 In the drought, we were all asked to NCVROSEE water. ______ 5

Find the four-letter word hidden at the end of one word and the beginning of the next word. The order of the letters may not be changed. B 21

Example The children had bats and balls. sand

21 The Vikings fled overland before regrouping. ______

22 Many frozen icecaps are found north of Canada. ______

23 Each term my school tests the fire alarm to make sure it is working. ______

24 Kevin ended the conversation fairly quickly. ______

25 Tom's biggest problem was the neighbours playing loud music. ______ 5

Change the first word of the third pair in the same way as the other pairs to give a new word. B 18

Example	bind, hind	bare, hare	but, hut
26	race, rate	face, fate	place, ______
27	can, cane	trip, tripe	prim, ______
28	port, sort	pane, sane	page, ______
29	stark, shark	stone, shone	stock, ______
30	file, life	pole, lope	ride, ______

5

Find and underline the two words which need to change places for each sentence to make sense. B 17

Example She went to letter the write.

31 When go you like to would to the zoo?

32 Nature is an amazing wonder of flying.

33 Island is an Britain nation in the continent of Europe.

34 I am planning to deposit fifty bank in the pounds.

35 Gabriel found that the heat about questions were extremely difficult to do. 5

Choose two words, one from each set of brackets, to complete the sentences in the best way. B 15

Example Tall is to (tree, short, colour) as narrow is to (thin, white, wide).

36 Sugar is to (grain, sweet, bitter) as lemon is to (lime, drink, sour).

37 True is to (argument, lie, truth) as vain is to (calm, preen, vanity).

38 Salad is to (can, fork, vegetables) as trifle is to (eat, pie, fruit).

39 Tooth is to (foot, mouth, clean) as brain is to (skull, nerves, blood).

40 Still is to (calm, active, fizzy) as movement is to (fast, motion, bubbly).

Fill in the crosswords so that all the given words are included. You have been given one letter as a clue in each crossword. B 19

41

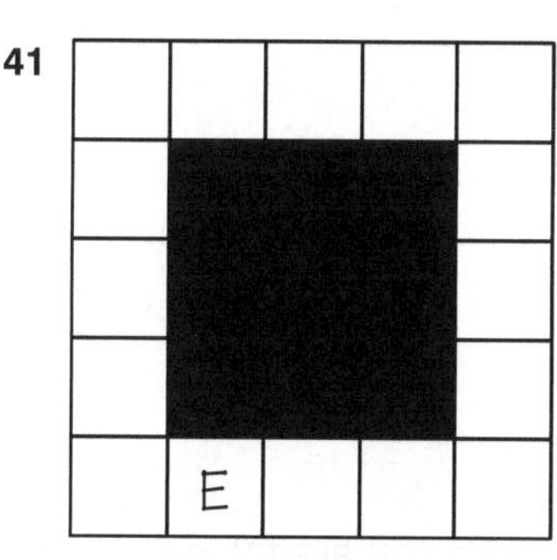

small, revel, tails, taper

42

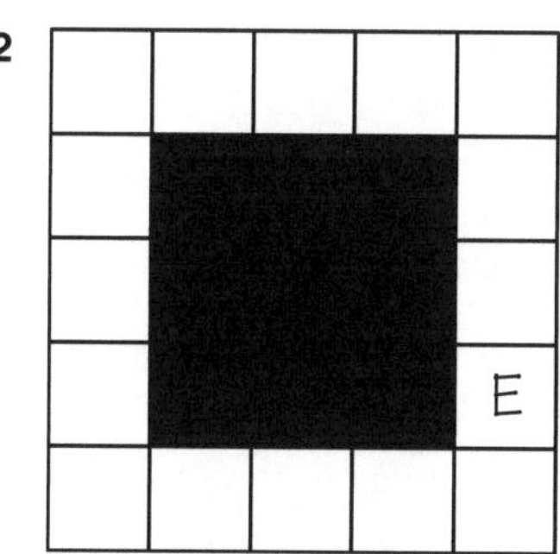

trays, place, paint, edges

43

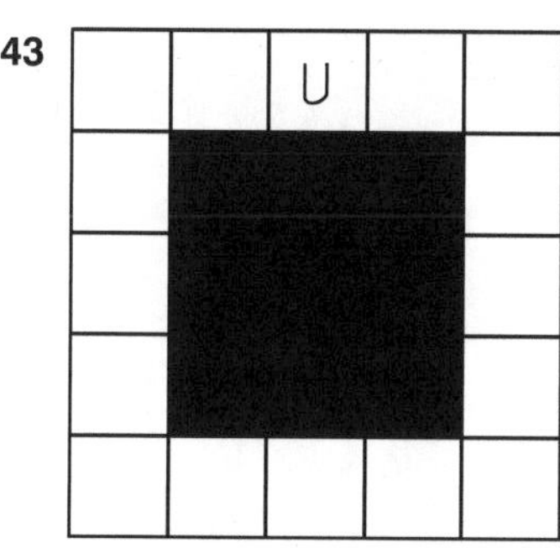

thick, falls, stick, fount

44

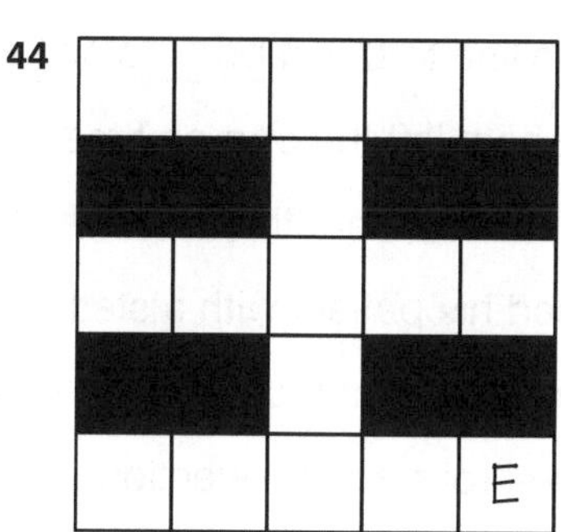

feeds, bride, taste, ideas

45

cures, moves, diver, wider

5

Rearrange the letters in capitals to make another word. The new word has something to do with the first two words or phrases. B 16

Example	spot	soil	SAINT	STAIN
46	final	end	SALT	______
47	prickle	bush	NORTH	______

48 story	yarn	LATE	______
49 rotten	not fresh	LEAST	______
50 servant	hard worker	VALES	______

5

If a = 10, b = 2, c = 3, d = 7, e = 5, give the answers to these calculations as letters. B 26

51 b + c + e = ______

52 be = ______

53 a – e = ______

54 (d – b) × b = ______

55 a ÷ b = ______

5

Change one word so that the sentence makes sense. Underline the word you are taking out and write your new word on the line. B 14

Example I waited in line to buy a book to see the film. ticket

56 The train for Birmingham left the port on time. ______

57 During the freezing summer months, snow fell almost daily. ______

58 The teacher examined his patient with a stethoscope. ______

59 Queen Victoria reigned for many days in the nineteenth century. ______

60 The florist sold loaves, rolls and a selection of cakes. ______

5

Rajeev buys three magazines every week. He likes magazines about pop music, computer games and television. Carl hates football, but buys a pop music magazine. Gill buys pop music and fashion magazines. Saskia does not buy any magazines. B 25

61 Which is the most popular magazine? ______

62 How many children buy computer game magazines? ______

2

Jan, Cilla, Vijay and Finn are friends. Finn and Vijay like gymnastics. The other children like hockey. Jan and Finn like tennis. Cilla's favourite is hockey, but she hates gymnastics. All but Finn like swimming. B 25

63 Which is the most popular sport? ______

64 Who likes gymnastics and swimming? ______

65 Who likes three sports? ______

3

Now go to the Progress Chart to record your score! Total 65

Paper 7

Underline the word in the brackets closest in meaning to the word in capitals. B 5

Example UNHAPPY (unkind death laughter sad friendly)

1 TRACK (music frame scale path bed)

2 FRAIL (weak lively success timely true)

3 SOFA (table settee television bunk pillow)

4 ANTIQUE (tasty ornament fresh steady old)

5 DOMESTICATED (famous wild tamed hunted criminal) 5

Underline the pair of words most opposite in meaning. B 9

Example	cup, mug	coffee, milk	hot, cold
6	spend, save	dye, colour	fall, drop
7	fly, float	advance, retreat	clue, hint
8	soak, wet	open, full	reckless, careful
9	flexible, rigid	gentle, soft	damp, moist
10	build, support	wind, crank	clutter, order

5

Find the letter which will end the first word and start the second word. B 10

Example peac (h) ome

11 fla ( ) ongue

12 mirro ( ) ain

13 cak ( ) nter

14 ove ( ) ew

15 fur ( ) ield 5

Find a word that can be put in front of each of the following words to make new, compound words. B 11

Example	CAST	FALL	WARD	POUR	DOWN
16	HILL	STAIRS	SET	KEEP	____
17	FALL	SHIRT	MARE	CLUB	____

18 MILL FALL MELON PROOF ______

19 HOUSE POST KEEPER WAY ______

20 STOP WAY FRAME MAN ______ 5

Find the four-letter word hidden at the end of one word and the beginning of the next word. The order of the letters may not be changed. B 21

Example The children had bats and balls. sand

21 Please replace that book on the shelf later. ______

22 That ornament would be extremely valuable if it were not damaged. ______

23 People of my age are often asked to give advice on living a long life. ______

24 The spies watched the suspects through binoculars. ______

25 It is clear that the sack needed some urgent repair. ______ 5

Change the first word into the last word, by changing one letter at a time and making a new, different word in the middle. B 13

Example CASE CASH LASH

26 FAST ______ FACE

27 FINE ______ FARE

28 TRAY ______ TRIP

29 FLEW ______ CLAW

30 BEST ______ BEAR 5

Complete the following sentences by selecting the most sensible word from each group of words given in the brackets. Underline the words selected. B 14

Example The (children, books, foxes) carried the (houses, books, steps) home from the greengrocer, library, factory).

31 The (cow, bird, girl) sat on its (nest, chair, floor), looking after its (chicks, cubs, hands).

32 The (lazy, late, first) man on the (river, moon, sun) wore a special (spacesuit, oar, cane).

33 The (pink, young, brown) leaves fell off the (cat, trees, sky) in (autumn, spring, grass).

34 A (rabbit, friend, doctor) has to (eat, march, train) for many (meals, lungs, years).

35 The fast moving (man, river, beaver) flowed (quickly, hungrily, lazily) to the (sky, race, sea). 5

Find and underline the two words which need to change places for each sentence to make sense. B 17

Example She went to <u>letter</u> the <u>write</u>.

36 You should never full with your mouth speak.

37 Can't have each we a piece of cake?

38 Health is good for your swimming.

39 It was a very pretty day on the warm beach.

40 The old car got into his battered man.

5

Complete the following expressions by filling in the missing word. B 15

Example Pen is to ink as brush is to paint

41 Box is to lid as house is to ________ .

42 Love is to hate as laugh is to ________ .

43 Tall is to taller as cool is to ________ .

44 Wales is to Welsh as Spain is to ________ .

45 Scarf is to neck as glove is to ________ .

5

Fill in the crosswords so that all the given words are included. You have been given one letter as a clue in each crossword. B 19

46

	■	■	■	
	■	■	■	
	■	■	■	
	O			

house, state, match, maids

47

	■	■	■	
	■	■	■	R
	■	■	■	

fight, flake, tiger, error

48

	O			
	■	■	■	
	■	■	■	
	■	■	■	

haunt, right, river, roach

49

■	■		■	■
		A		
■	■		■	■

sites, plait, aspen, avail

50 

dress, trees, cider, tasty

5

If a = 2, b = 4, c = 6, d = 8 and e = 12, find the value of the following calculations. B 26

51 $e + b =$ ______

52 $e - a =$ ______

53 $a \times b =$ ______

54 $(e - d) + c =$ ______

55 $\frac{d}{b} =$ ______ 5

Rearrange the letters in capitals to make another word. The new word has something to do with the first two words. B 16

Examples	spot	soil	SAINT	STAIN
56	javelin	point	REAPS	______
57	begin	commence	TARTS	______
58	tassle	edge	FINGER	______
59	quiet	hushed	LISTEN	______
60	support	love	RACE	______

5

Choose the word or phrase that makes each sentence true. B 14

Example A LIBRARY always has (posters, a carpet, books, DVDs, stairs).

61 A SHOP always has (carpets, goods, dresses, women, stairs).

62 A BANK always has (customers, men, pictures, mirrors, money).

63 A PARTY always has (music, food, balloons, guests, gifts).

64 A GARDEN always has (flowers, a bench, trees, earth, a swing).

65 A FLORIST always has (balloons, toys, flowers, chocolates, trees). 5

Now go to the Progress Chart to record your score! Total 65

Paper 1

1 test, exam
2 rot, decay
3 eat, consume
4 light, pale
5 extend, enlarge
6 then, now
7 large, tiny
8 loose, tight
9 hollow, solid
10 first, final
11 teacher, children, lunches
12 try, swimming, tide
13 cows, huddled, field
14 team, goal, match
15 whisked, dessert, fork
16 SHADES, DASHES
17 TEARS, RATES
18 PEARS, SPEAR
19 FLESH, SHELF
20 STEAL, LEAST
21 tear
22 carp
23 loan
24 moon
25 calm
26 e
27 t
28 m
29 r
30 p
31 lake, boat
32 you, I
33 mechanic, car
34 is, do
35 caged, angry
36 TU
37 XV
38 NO
39 Z11
40 CE
41 b
42 s
43 m
44 y
45 a
46

S	H	A	R	K
T				N
A				E
R				E
T	I	L	E	S

47

F	R	O	N	T
R				R
E				I
S				E
H	E	A	D	S

48

A	B	O	V	E
L				L
O				V
F				E
T	U	F	T	S

49

R	U	P	E	E
O				M
U				P
N				T
D	A	I	S	Y

50

G	R	U	E	L
R				A
A				U
N				G
D	O	U	G	H

51 * – : &
52 $ – : *
53 & – : £ –
54 TAR
55 TAINT
56 tamed
57 every
58 matted
59 games
60 dimmer
61 groan
62 Fettle
63 Hambury
64 16 km
65 1 km

Paper 2

1 build, construct
2 put, place
3 attempt, try
4 grave, serious
5 easy, effortless
6 false, true
7 continuous, ended
8 plain, elegant
9 criticise, praise
10 well, ill
11 flatmate
12 attack
13 forsake
14 outcry
15 invest
16 ROT
17 LOW
18 MAT
19 ONE
20 ATE
21 here
22 rope
23 rare
24 play
25 ease
26 POSH
27 SEAR
28 LOST
29 MINE
30 STAG
31 arrive, holiday, resort
32 way, go, theatre
33 learner, stalling, engine
34 haunted, castle, spirit
35 mathematics, graphs, numbers
36 Thursday, Saturday
37 sailing, ship
38 shore, lake
39 restricted, unlimited
40 considerate, generous
41

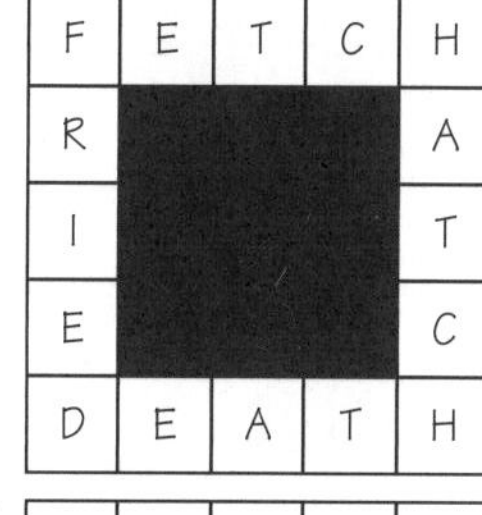

F	E	T	C	H
R				A
I				T
E				C
D	E	A	T	H

42

G	R	I	N	D
O				I
A				A
T				R
S	T	O	R	Y

43

B	R	O	W	N
A				I
T				G
H				H
E	L	E	C	T

44
45

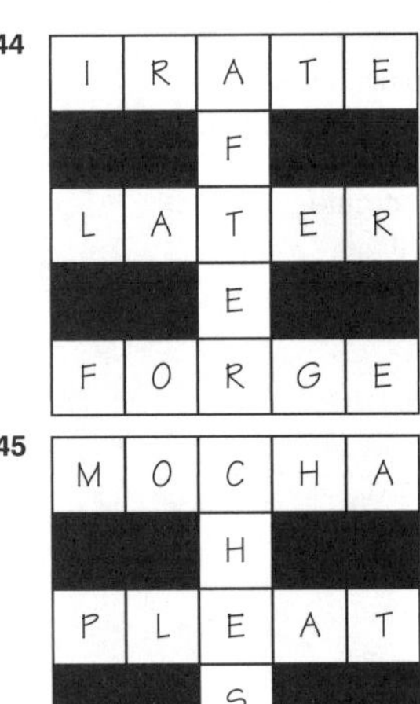

46 54
47 21
48 7
49 25
50 16
51 < > ? ? %
52 ? £ % X
53 % X > <
54 ILL
55 CALL
56 drained
57 plank
58 version
59 nearest
60 plain
61 4
62 England
63 Eleanor
64 2 km
65 Jessica and Lianne

Paper 3

1 drag
2 butterfly
3 apple
4 agreement
5 Russia
6 love, hate
7 hard, effortless
8 waste, conserve
9 fair, dark
10 infinite, limited
11 e
12 e
13 l
14 o
15 n
16 DOOR
17 STAND
18 TIME
19 NEWS
20 HEART
21 send
22 seem
23 area
24 cart
25 sage
26 have, could
27 computer, school
28 four, two
29 steal, right
30 China, world
31 3
32 55
33 16
34 23
35 27

36

P	A	I	N	T
R				H
I				E
C				I
E	N	T	E	R

37

S	T	A	N	D
H				R
A				A
D				F
E	V	E	N	T

38

F L A I R
A E
I I
N G
T H O R N

39

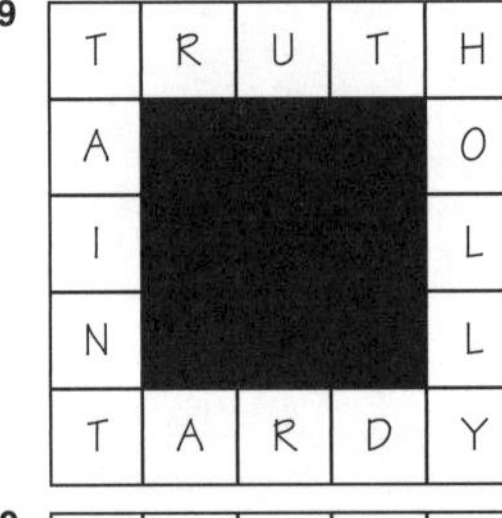

40

41 aged, young
42 shoe, leather
43 lessen, multiply
44 change, remain
45 unique, original
46 ‘ £ $ %
47 £ & * ^
48 BALL
49 BEAN
50 ACHE
51 relay
52 alert
53 rested
54 starve
55 ignore
56 James
57 Soraya, Lena
58 Kim
59 4
60 2
61 WALK
62 FINAL
63 LESSON
64 SPENT
65 LETTERS

Paper 4

1 push, shove
2 weep, cry
3 mend, repair
4 control, manage
5 uphold, support
6 DIN
7 HAM
8 ARM
9 INK
10 MAN
11 k
12 e
13 y
14 m
15 e
16 OUT
17 IRON
18 SNOW
19 EYE
20 POST
21 chin
22 meal
23 idea
24 dead
25 heap
26 but
27 rice
28 steer
29 fare
30 leap
31 girl, school, first
32 taking, test, week
33 climbing, dangerous, weather
34 wondered, try, assistance

35 never, brush, teeth
36 woman, time
37 been, have
38 the, all
39 tell, time
40 that, why
41 ninth
42 French
43 century
44 down
45 wet
46 O, R
47 DG, DH
48 D9, F13
49 UF, OL
50 ZY, VU
51 LGAC
52 TWIG
53 MQRO
54 ZDLW
55 HSK
56 cola
57 Siobhan
58 Bangor
59 5
60 27
61 32
62 5 years
63 4
64 2
65 8

Paper 5

1–5 Give one mark for each two correct answers: skipping G, basket C, Cluedo G, urn C, den H, flat H, cup C, lodge H, casket C, snakes and ladders G.
6 ROT
7 MEN
8 ASH
9 PEN
10 ACT
11 d
12 l
13 t
14 s
15 w
16 Ⓜ
17 Ⓘ
18 Ⓛ
19 Ⓣ
20 Ⓞ
21 herb
22 reap
23 lord
24 pint
25 fare
26 never
27 stripe
28 cheap
29 through
30 wrested
31 two, four, eight
32 strong, broken
33 shop, chocolate, cakes
34 would, try, uniform
35 shot, unseen, army
36 whisper, quiet
37 head, hands
38 rule, teach
39 colour, measurement
40 impressive, plain
41

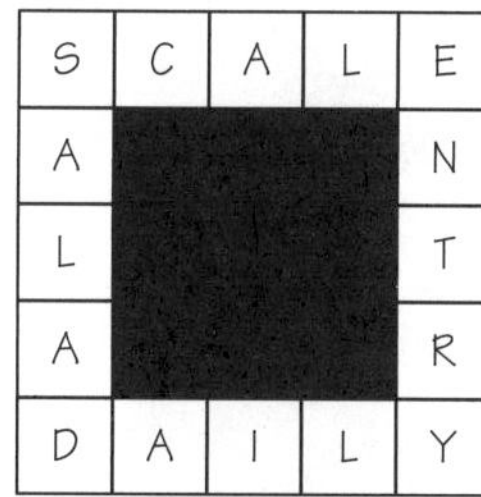

42

W I N D Y
A A
T R
E D
R I N G S

43

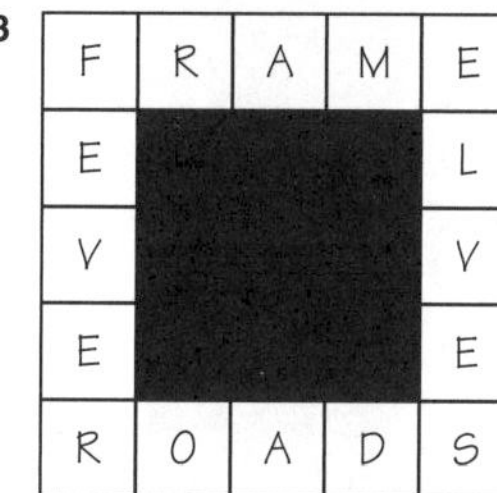

44

M I S E R
U
F U N N Y
N
T R Y S T

45

46 MFWFM
47 MFBWF
48 FWFS
49 RARE
50 LIST
51 b
52 b
53 d
54 b
55 f
56 legs
57 wet
58 a roof
59 a border
60 hard
61 father
62 daughter
63 granddaughter
64 niece
65 father-in-law

Paper 6

1 gift, present
2 top, peak
3 follow, pursue
4 please, delight
5 judgement, decision
6 PEA
7 TIP
8 WHO
9 TAN
10 MEN
11 t
12 y
13 e
14 k
15 t
16 QUARTER
17 REVERSED
18 GRAVY
19 PLAYERS
20 CONSERVE
21 dove
22 nice
23 real
24 vine
25 then
26 plate
27 prime
28 sage
29 shock
30 dire
31 go, would
32 Nature, flying
33 Island, Britain
34 bank, pounds
35 heat, questions
36 sweet, sour
37 truth, vanity
38 vegetables, fruit
39 mouth, skull
40 calm, motion

41

42

P	L	A	C	E
A				D
I				G
N				E
T	R	A	Y	S

43

F	O	U	N	T
A				H
L				I
L				C
S	T	I	C	K

44

B	R	I	D	E
		D		
F	E	E	D	S
		A		
T	A	S	T	E

45

W	I	D	E	R
		I		
M	O	V	E	S
		E		
C	U	R	E	S

46 LAST
47 THORN
48 TALE
49 STALE
50 SLAVE
51 a
52 a
53 e
54 a
55 e
56 port, station
57 summer, winter
58 teacher, doctor
59 days, years
60 florist, baker
61 pop music
62 1
63 swimming
64 Vijay
65 Jan

Paper 7

1 path
2 weak
3 settee
4 old
5 tamed
6 spend, save
7 advance, retreat
8 reckless, careful
9 flexible, rigid
10 clutter, order
11 t
12 r
13 e
14 n
15 y
16 UP
17 NIGHT
18 WATER
19 GATE
20 DOOR
21 flat
22 torn
23 gear
24 swat
25 knee
26 FACT
27 FIRE
28 TRAP
29 FLAW
30 BEAT
31 bird, nest, chicks
32 first, moon, spacesuit
33 brown, trees, autumn
34 doctor, train, years
35 river, quickly, sea
36 full, speak
37 have, we
38 health, swimming
39 pretty, warm
40 car, man
41 roof
42 cry
43 cooler
44 Spanish
45 hand

46

M	A	I	D	S
A				T
T				A
C				T
H	O	U	S	E

47

F	L	A	K	E
I				R
G				R
H				O
T	I	G	E	R

48

R	O	A	C	H
I				A
V				U
E				N
R	I	G	H	T

49

A	S	P	E	N
		L		
A	V	A	I	L
		I		
S	I	T	E	S

50

C	I	D	E	R
		R		
T	R	E	E	S
		S		
T	A	S	T	Y

51 16
52 10
53 8
54 10
55 2
56 SPEAR
57 START
58 FRINGE
59 SILENT
60 CARE
61 goods
62 money
63 guests

64 earth
65 flowers

Paper 8

1–5 *Give one mark for each two correct answers:* noun B, monitor C, verb B, violin A, disk drive C, mouse C, guitar A, preposition B, piano A, flute A.

6 pull, push
7 wild, tame
8 shut, open
9 combine, separate
10 friend, enemy
11 s
12 y
13 l
14 t
15 l
16 takeaway
17 update
18 blameless
19 office
20 peanut
21 wasp
22 bush
23 thin
24 seat
25 army
26 RICE
27 MEAT
28 PLAY
29 FLAT
30 BEAR
31 O15
32 YW
33 FI
34 PD
35 MO
36

T	R	U	S	T
A				H
M				O
E				S
S	H	O	V	E

37

P	R	I	Z	E
R				V
E				E
S				R
S	U	N	N	Y

38

I	C	I	N	G
N				R
P				A
U				V
T	A	N	G	Y

39

U	L	T	R	A
		Y		
H	A	P	P	Y
		E		
H	A	S	T	Y

40

F	U	N	N	Y
		I		
R	I	G	H	T
		H		
T	I	T	L	E

41 sort
42 play
43 fly
44 stab
45 kid
46 TIE
47 MAT
48 RED
49 LEAP
50 TALE
51 blue team
52 15
53 10
54 Tuesday
55 14
56 e
57 b
58 c
59 f
60 b
61 EGILMNT
62 T
63 G
64 ARSTY
65 S

Paper 9

1 bread
2 right
3 bold
4 scream
5 amazed
6 sad
7 raise
8 arrive
9 exclude
10 join
11 RUM
12 RAN
13 OWN
14 ARM
15 TEA
16 undertake
17 upright
18 throughout
19 downstairs
20 cupboard
21 then
22 bite
23 send
24 pout
25 mask
26 fit, flame
27 word, tolls
28 mile, self
29 able, scarf
30 rob, event
31 goalkeeper, save, match
32 eat, vegetables, good
33 old, walk, stick
34 dress, modern, belt
35 time, ancient, witch
36 huge, short
37 early, excited
38 crowded, bare
39 fasten, twist
40 rest, stay
41

Q	U	I	L	L
U				A
E				R
E				G
R	A	N	G	E

42

F	L	O	O	R
R				H
I				Y
E				M
D	R	A	P	E

43

C	R	E	P	E
H				R
E				A
E				S
R	I	F	L	E

44

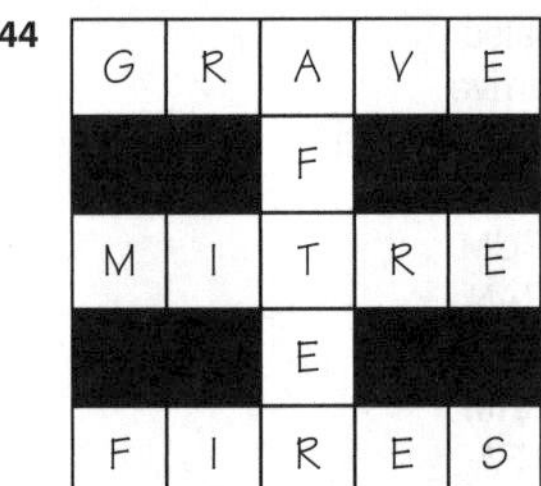

45

B	I	T	E	S
■	■	R	■	■
T	H	A	N	K
■	■	P	■	■
T	A	S	T	E

46 PK, PM
47 M, S
48 Q9, O11
49 OJ, RH
50 KM, PH
51 7325
52 5237
53 5247
54 1352
55 1852
56 ACJKOPST
57 T
58 K
59 CNORTUY
60 T
61 Jem
62 10
63 English
64 German
65 Italian

Paper 10

1 sponge, ship
2 twig, nest
3 heart, friend
4 next, future
5 undecided, complicated
6 INK
7 TEN
8 PAR
9 LIT
10 OUR
11 rot
12 dice
13 deal
14 bear
15 treat
16 bare
17 torn
18 fear
19 hall
20 arch
21 late, cramp
22 prim, gape
23 tile, sight
24 stand, brought
25 mine, clay
26 lunch
27 sly
28 knock
29 poke
30 green
31 horse, hay, stable
32 night, hooting, distance
33 road, ways, traffic
34 teacher, pupils, homework
35 girls, mother, cinema
36 outside, rainy
37 year, day
38 month, first
39 lunch, lasagne
40 mother, baby
41 LN
42 S19
43 OP
44 WU
45 TV
46 quick, slow
47 save, spend
48 attack, retreat
49 near, distant
50 specific, general
51–55 citsilaer, taerter, tcane, tcarter, tsomla
56 612
57 9123
58 9136
59 SURE
60 HUES
61 toffee and fudge
62 chocolate and sweets
63 Eric
64 Ann
65 Farook

Paper 11

1 cheerful, happy
2 disappear, vanish
3 flash, flare
4 career, profession
5 pay, salary
6 ROW
7 RAW
8 KIN
9 SIT
10 TAR
11 HOUSE
12 SEA
13 DOWN
14 BACK
15 WATCH
16 hate
17 ants
18 sour
19 slay
20 rope
21 GALE
22 POST OR PART
23 BEST
24 CREW
25 SPAR
26 radio, music
27 reach, managed
28 month, day
29 hunting, lions
30 queue, wait

31

S	T	U	N	T
L	■	■	■	H
E	■	■	■	E
E	■	■	■	S
P	L	A	C	E

32

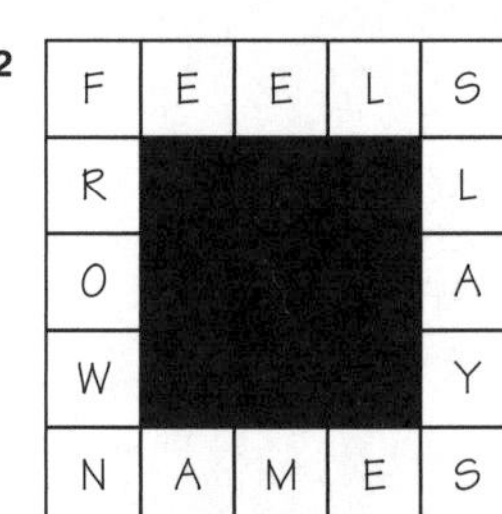

33

34

S	E	V	E	N
■	■	E	■	■
P	R	I	S	M
■	■	L	■	■
H	A	S	T	E

35 

36 AK, AM
37 OS, RV
38 LI, NK
39 DQ, DO
40 IR, HS
41 ♦ ○ • ♥
42 & ♥ ♦ ○ •
43 ○ • ♥ ♦ ▲
44 HEAR
45 RATE
46–47 Eagles eat mice. Eagles are predators
48–49 Spain is hot. Palm trees never grow in cold countries.
50–51 Earth is further from the Sun than Venus. Venus is hotter than Earth.
52 *Eastenders*
53 Joaquin
54 Molly
55 Rashid and Tom
56 t
57 q
58 s
59 r
60 u
61 PCKN
62 QDRS
63 GOOD
64 BSX
65 QLRDE

Paper 12

1 smart, fast
2 body, smile
3 mud, sand
4 desert, ocean
5 field, meadow
6 PEN
7 PIP
8 ADD
9 EAR
10 APE
11 y
12 r
13 t
14 r
15 l
16 netball
17 flatmate
18 pattern
19 goodwill
20 manage
21 hiss
22 mane
23 pear
24 tilt
25 vein
26 self, shell
27 brow, shone
28 hare, smash
29 rate, pact
30 last, tone
31 trees, leaves
32 race, first
33 bowl, breakfast
34 silver, gold
35 find, dig
36 HX
37 QN
38 WM
39 WD
40 JQ
41 3491
42 3428
43 3528
44 2849
45 2528
46 Li
47 cat and dog
48 Sharif
49 2
50 5
51 h
52 h
53 f
54 d
55 h
56 flower, petrol
57 garage, vet
58 moon's, sun's
59 foot, neck
60 marshmallow, cream
61 UDWHV
62 RNWO
63 SALE
64 SHOW
65 PDVN

Paper 13

1 B
2 D
3 C
4 A
5 B
6 hunt, search
7 similar, alike
8 overtake, pass
9 show, display
10 vague, unclear
11 pass
12 conflict
13 damage
14 follow
15 doubtful
16 can
17 light
18 hit
19 bright
20 smart
21 GREEN
22 WOOD
23 FIRE
24 HAND
25 HAIR
26 sand
27 lace
28 torn
29 term
30 fort
31 man
32 sore
33 plot
34 hop
35 rip
36 bake, oven
37 Bindy, Annabel
38 homework, fingers
39 red, wild
40 red, read
41 e
42 h
43 r
44 t
45 k
46 3115
47 8277
48 2751
49 5117
50 3297
51 David
52 Peter
53 16
54 23
55 Town D
56 PAIRS
57 EXITS
58 SAUCE
59 SAGE
60 DANGER
61 butcher, baker
62 tame, wild
63 hole, nest
64 Sunday, December
65 nurse, teacher

Paper 14

1 swift, fast
2 back, rear
3 miniature, small
4 aim, goal
5 pole, rod

6 brilliant, dull
7 rude, polite
8 rise, fall
9 criticise, praise
10 relaxed, tense
11 plain
12 grace
13 pack
14 grain
15 star
16 e
17 t
18 d
19 k
20 p
21 hole
22 edge
23 cane
24 this
25 rind
26 PART
27 MIST
28 SOAR
29 BRAT
30 CUTS
31 TEST
32 ALSO
33 PEAR
34 PINT
35 RARE
36 r
37 e
38 t
39 t
40 b
41 pound, beat
42 lower, reduce
43 injure, damage
44 sickness, illness
45 tough, strong
46 WAR
47 WATER
48 WEATHER
49 PASS
50 BACK
51 QN, UN
52 CC, XX
53 RP, PN
54 PO, PQ
55 I5, K6
56 PEAR
57 CLAP
58 PALE
59 LEER
60 PALACE
61 wake, sleep
62 notes, strings
63 alive, dead
64 moon, sun
65 hungry, full

Paper 15

1 ask, request
2 shiny, glistening
3 destroyed, broken
4 cross, angry
5 drum, tap
6 shy, confident
7 cause, effect
8 light, heavy
9 tired, energetic
10 rare, common
11 r
12 b
13 l
14 r
15 y
16 lone
17 shun
18 cast
19 itch
20 heat
21 b
22 c
23 t
24 f
25 w
26 dragon
27 cove
28 ration
29 shin
30 meter
31 track, train
32 England, Kent
33 films, music
34 home, late
35 house, newspaper
36 slow, high
37 overlook, honour
38 water, coal
39 wet, cold
40 bird, mammal
41 10
42 45
43 E
44 E
45 D
46 m
47 y
48 e
49 d
50 l
51 LEAP
52 FALSE
53 WEAK
54 ANGERS
55 MELON
56 PAST
57 MACE or MITE
58 ARMS
59 SNIP
60 FLAW
61 EO
62 WW
63 ST
64 ZV
65 Z26

Paper 8

Look at these groups of words. B 1

A	B	C
Musical instruments	Parts of speech	Computer terms

1–5 Choose the correct group for each of the words below. Write in the letter.

noun ___ monitor ___ verb ___ violin ___ disk drive ___

mouse ___ guitar ___ preposition ___ piano ___ flute ___ 5

Underline the pair of words most opposite in meaning. B 9

Example cup, mug coffee, milk hot, cold

6 start, begin pull, push fight, battle

7 wild, tame medium, middle stale, old

8 shut, open tight, cramped fix, mend

9 try, attempt combine, separate stay, remain

10 filter, flow friend, enemy bump, knock 5

Find the letter that will end the first word and start the second word. B 10

Example peac (h) ome

11 dres (___) ign

12 pla (___) oke

13 shal (___) ove

14 trai (___) iara

15 dril (___) ong 5

Underline the two words, one from each group, that go together to form a new word. The word in the first group always comes first. B 8

Example (hand, green, for) (light, house, sure)

16 (take, bring, seat) (home, away, back)

17 (up, in, at) (day, week, date)

18 (hunt, weak, blame) (on, less, full)

19 (on, off, down) (rest, step, ice)

20 (snap, pea, spice) (nut, bag, hot) 5

Find the four-letter word hidden at the end of one word and the beginning of the next word. The order of the letters may not be changed. B 21

Example The children had bats and balls. sand

21 Joe was pleased he didn't have any homework that night. ______

22 We were surprised when the bus halted at the stop. ______

23 Mark felt proud of himself for finishing fourth in the race. ______

24 Apples eaten quickly will give you indigestion. ______

25 The car my brother just bought is bright red. ______ 5

Change the first word into the last word, by changing one letter at a time and making a new, different word in the middle. B 13

Example CASE CASH LASH

26 NICE ______ RACE

27 SEAT ______ MOAT

28 PLAN ______ SLAY

29 FEAT ______ FLAY

30 BEAN ______ TEAR 5

Fill in the missing letters and numbers. The alphabet has been written out to help you. B 23

A B C D E F G H I J K L M N O P Q R S T U V W X Y Z

Example AB is to CD as PQ is to RS

31 C3 is to E5 as M13 is to ______

32 WU is to TR as BZ is to ______

33 HK is to MP as AD is to ______

34 RR is to XL as JJ is to ______

35 AC is to EG as IK is to ______ 5

Fill in the crosswords so that all the given words are included. You have been given one letter as a clue in each crossword. B 19

36

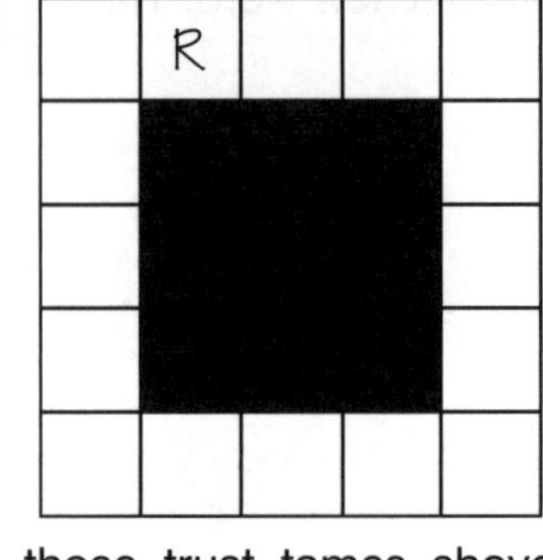

those, trust, tames, shove

37

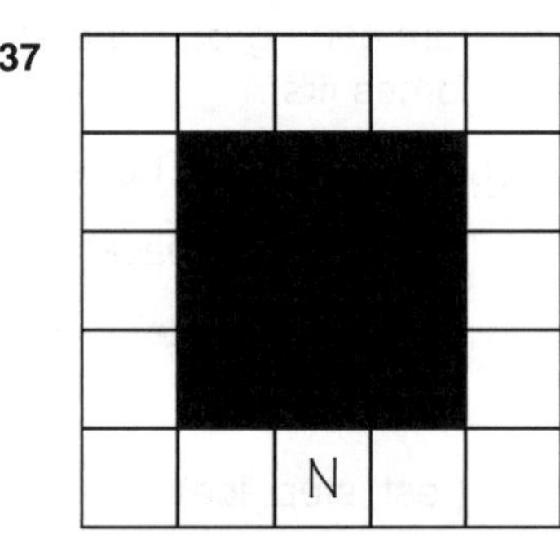

press, prize, every, sunny

38 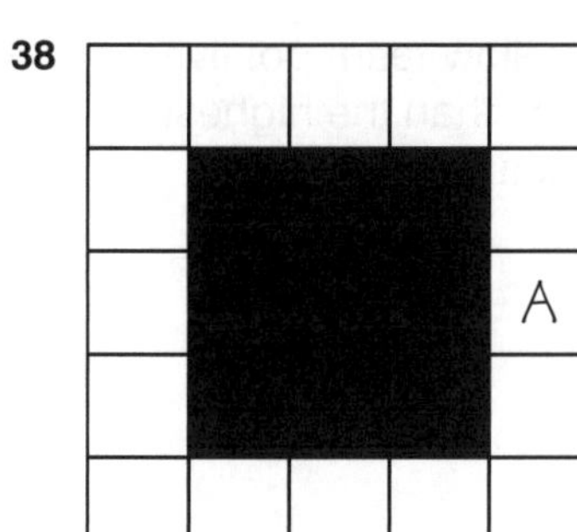
gravy, input, tangy, icing

39 
types, ultra, hasty, happy

40 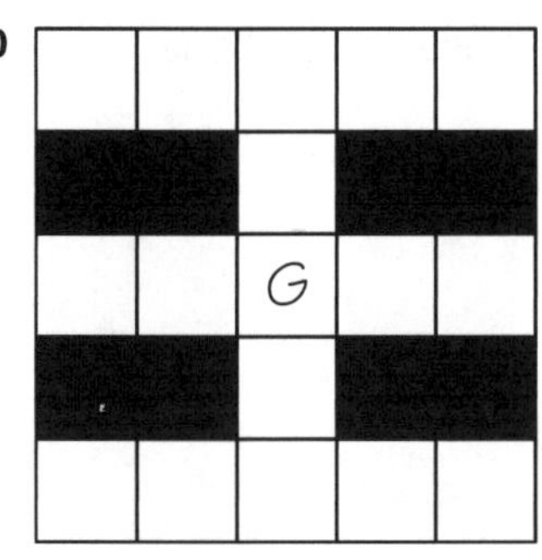
right, title, funny, night

5

Underline the one word in brackets which will go equally well with both pairs of words outside the brackets. B 5

Example rush, attack cost, fee (price, hasten, strike, charge, money)

41 kind, type select, choose (sort, gentle, take, pass, soft)

42 frolic, romp performance, drama (joy, act, jump, play, game)

43 insect, bug travel, aeroplane (fly, ant, hear, floor, listen)

44 attempt, try knife, jab (go, sword, stab, stake, point)

45 child, young tease, fool (kid, trick, badger, fox, tail) 5

46 If 7345 stands for TIME, 735 stands for ____________. B 24

47 If 2839 stands for TAME, 382 stands for ____________.

48 If 4337 stands for DEER, 734 stands for ____________.

49 If 6913 stands for PEAL, 3916 stands for ____________.

50 If 4321 stands for LATE, 2341 stands for ____________. 5

In a class athletics competition, the blue team scored 20 points. The yellow team got five points more than the red team. The green team scored eight points less than the highest of these teams. The red team scored half as many points as the blue team.

B 25

51 Which team came top? ____________

52 How many points did the yellow team score? ____________

53 How many points did the red team score? ____________

54 If it was Tuesday two days ago, what day will it be in five days' time? ____________

55 If David will be 23 in four years' time, how old was he five years ago? ____________

5

If a = 2, b = 4, c = 8, d = 6, e = 10 and f = 12, give the answers to these calculations as letters.

B 26

56 a + c = ___

57 f − c = ___

58 a × b = ___

59 a + b + d = ___

60 c ÷ a = ___

5

Answer these questions. The alphabet has been written out to help you.

B 20

A B C D E F G H I J K L M N O P Q R S T U V W X Y Z

61 Put the letters in MELTING in alphabetical order. ____________

62 Which is now the last letter? ____________

63 Which is now the second letter? ____________

64 Put the letters in TRAYS in alphabetical order. ____________

65 Which is now the third letter? ____________

5

Now go to the Progress Chart to record your score! **Total** 65

Paper 9

Find a word that is similar in meaning to the word in capital letters and that rhymes with the second word.

B 5

Example CABLE tyre wire

1 LOAF head ____________

2 CORRECT flight ____________

3 BRAVE	hold	________
4 SHOUT	dream	________
5 SURPRISED	glazed	________

5

Underline the one word in the brackets which is most opposite in meaning to the word in capitals. B 6

Example	WIDE	(broad	vague	long	narrow	motorway)
6	JOYFUL	(old	rich	cheerful	sad	rested)
7	LOWER	(drop	raise	down	deep	below)
8	LEAVE	(behind	right	arrive	go	exit)
9	INCLUDE	(accept	exclude	add	remain	contain)
10	SEPARATE	(shrink	reduce	divide	apart	join)

5

Find the three-letter word which can be added to the letters in capitals to make a new word. The new word will complete the sentence sensibly. B 22

Example The cat sprang onto the MO. USE

11 The musicians enjoyed playing their TPETS loudly. ________

12 The food was very good at the Italian RESTAUT. ________

13 The museum contained many royal CRS and robes. ________

14 The choir was singing in perfect HONY. ________

15 The swimming CHER asked the students to dive into the pool. ________

5

Underline two words, one from each group, that go together to form a new word. The word in the first group always comes first. B 8

Example (hand, green, for) (light, house, sure)

16 (under, side, on) (take, put, out)

17 (to, where, up) (good, right, may)

18 (at, through, in) (out, last, fire)

19 (side, down, on) (stairs, case, ladder)

20 (glass, drink, cup) (board, set, light)

5

Find the four-letter word hidden at the end of one word and the beginning of the next word. The order of the letters may not be changed. B 21

Example The children had bats and balls. sand

21 We will be the next group to get a table. ________

22 Kate's rabbit enjoys munching on lettuce and carrots. ________

23 Our holiday to Mauritius ended on a Saturday. ________

24 It is difficult to skip outside in the long grass. ________

25 My mum asked everyone to be quiet because the baby was sleeping. ________

5

Move one letter from the first word and add it to the second word to make two new words.

B 13

Example hunt sip <u>hut</u> <u>snip</u>

26 flit fame ______ ______

27 sword toll ______ ______

28 smile elf ______ ______

29 fable scar ______ ______

30 robe vent ______ ______

5

Complete the following sentences by selecting the most sensible word from each group of words given in the brackets. Underline the words selected.

B 14

Example The (<u>children</u>, books, foxes) carried the (houses, <u>books</u>, steps) home from the (greengrocer, <u>library</u>, factory).

31 The (score, goalkeeper, spectator) made a wonderful (save, fall, trick) to make sure we won the (treat, match, race).

32 (Eat, wash, dry) up your (water, vegetables, shoes) because they are (late, old, good) for you.

33 He was very (late, hungry, old) and found it hard to (dive, eat, walk) without a (dish, stick, paper).

34 Her (foot, dress, head) was very (modern, flat, wet) and had a wide (belt, eye, pot) on it.

35 Once upon a (day, year, time) in an (empty, ancient, easy) cottage there lived an old (witch, apple, child).

5

Choose two words, one from each set of brackets, to complete the sentences in the best way.

B 15

Example Tall is to (tree, <u>short</u>, colour) as narrow is to (thin, white, <u>wide</u>).

36 Tiny is to (wild, small, huge) as long is to (last, little, short).

37 Late is to (first, early, behind) as calm is to (excited, easy, afraid).

38 Full is to (none, crowded, alone) as empty is to (bare, last, food).

39 Tie is to (shirt, bump, fasten) as turn is to (twist, knob, first).

40 Pause is to (continue, rest, worry) as remain is to (stay, important, leftover).

5

Fill in the crosswords so that all the given words are included. You have been given one letter as a clue in each crossword.

B 19

41

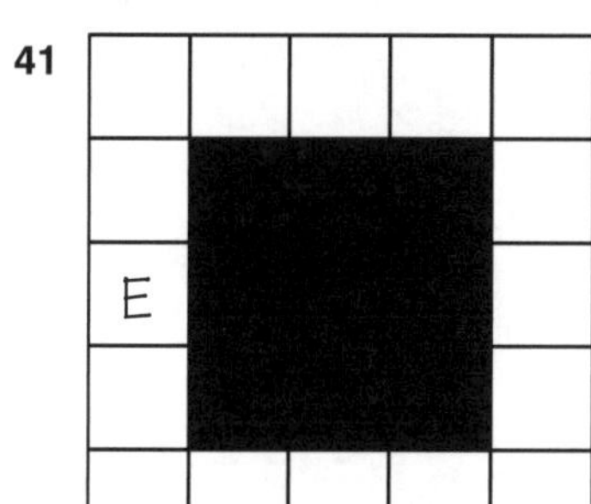

large, queer, range, quill

42

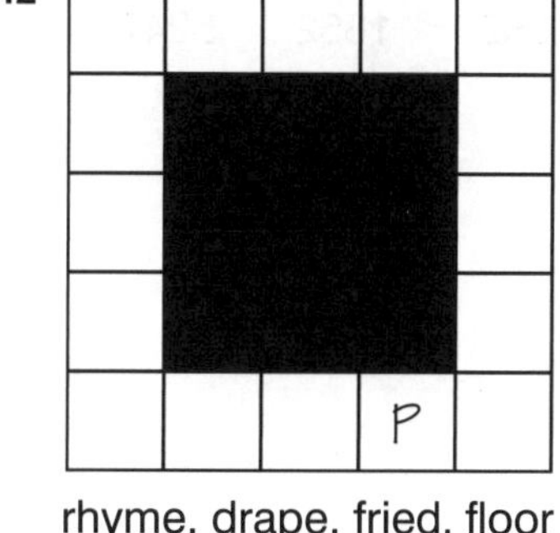

rhyme, drape, fried, floor

43

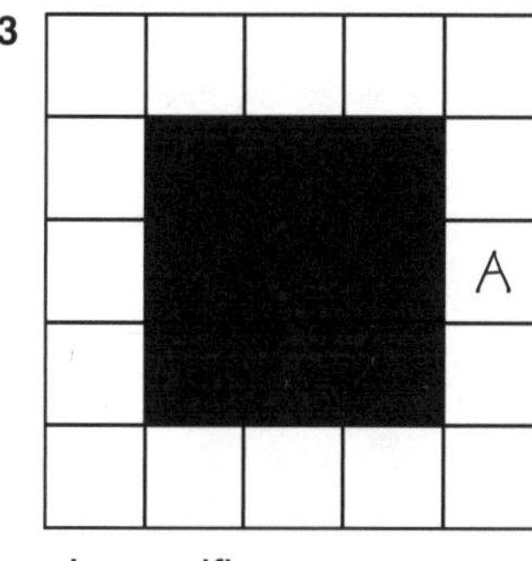

cheer, rifle, crepe, erase

44

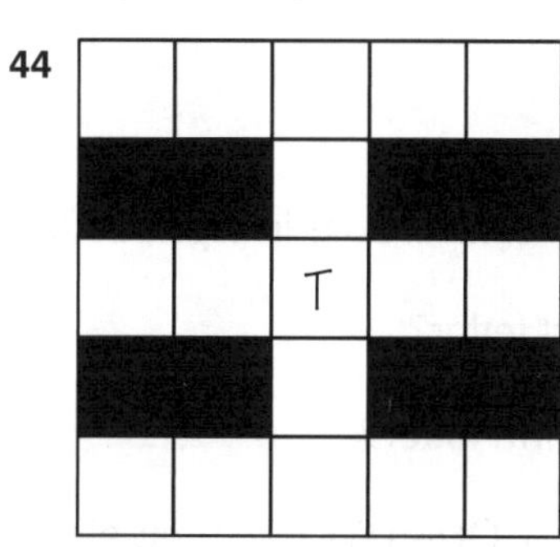

fires, after, mitre, grave

45

thank, bites, taste, traps

5

Give the missing letters and numbers in the following sequences. The alphabet has been written out to help you.

B 23

A B C D E F G H I J K L M N O P Q R S T U V W X Y Z

Example	CQ	DQ	EP	FP	GO	HO
46	PC	PE	PG	PI	__	__
47	D	G	J	__	P	__
48	Y1	W3	U5	S7	__	__
49	CR	FP	IN	LL	__	__
50	AW	BV	DT	GQ	__	__

5

Here are the number codes for five words. Match the right word to the right code. B 24

PAST	STAR	RATS	STIR	POST
5237	7325	1352	1852	5247

51 RATS ______

52 STAR ______

53 STIR ______

54 PAST ______

55 POST ______ 5

56 Arrange the letters in JACKPOTS in alphabetical order. ______ B 20

57 Which is now the last letter? ______

58 Which is now the fourth letter? ______

59 Arrange the letters in COUNTRY in alphabetical order. ______

60 Which is now the fifth letter? ______ 5

Three little cats are called Jim, Jam and Jem. Jim is three years younger than Jam, but is two years older than Jem, who is five. B 25

61 Who is the youngest? ______

62 How old is Jam? ______ 2

Jean, Malek, Geeta, Martin and Sophie are students. Jean and Geeta speak English, German and Spanish. Sophie speaks Italian and German. Martin and Malek speak German, Italian and Spanish. B 25

63 Which language is spoken by the fewest children? ______

64 Which language is spoken by the most children? ______

65 Which language is spoken by three children? ______ 3

Now go to the Progress Chart to record your score! Total 65

Paper 10

Underline the two words which are the odd ones out in the following groups of words. B 4

Example	black	<u>king</u>	purple	green	<u>house</u>
1	sponge	lake	ship	sea	ocean
2	crow	pigeon	twig	nest	eagle
3	love	heart	adore	friend	admire
4	next	aged	future	elderly	old
5	undecided	complicated	conclusion	termination	end

5

Find the three-letter word which can be added to the letters in capitals to make a new word. The new word will complete the sentence sensibly. B 22

Example The cat sprang onto the MO. USE

6 Please DR up your juice. ______

7 The meal lay half EA on the table. ______

8 I think that you should COME the two options. ______

9 Being POE is just good manners. ______

10 I went to the paint shop with my Dad to decide which COL I wanted to paint my room. ______

5

Underline the one word which **can be made** from the letters of the word in capital letters. B 7

Example	CHAMPION	camping	notch	peach	cramp	<u>chimp</u>
11	CONTROL	rot	cannot	call	roll	room
12	DECISION	slide	diesel	noisy	dice	scent
13	SLANDEROUS	gland	race	deal	slate	ended
14	INTOLERABLE	stale	strain	stable	bear	blame
15	ALLITERATION	creation	terrain	alight	terrapin	treat

5

Find the four-letter word hidden at the end of one word and the beginning of the next word. The order of the letters may not be changed. B 21

Example The children had bats and balls. sand

16 Mum replied that Jake and Caleb aren't playing today. ______

17 The zoo's alligator never came out of the pool except for food. ______

18 In those days a serf earned his living with great difficulty. ____

19 It is important to catch all shots coming in his direction. ____

20 The star changed shape when looked at through the telescope. ____

5

Move one letter from the first word and add it to the second word to make two new words.

B 13

Example hunt sip *hut* *snip*

21 plate cram ____ ____

22 prime gap ____ ____

23 title sigh ____ ____

24 strand bought ____ ____

25 mince lay ____ ____

5

Find a word that is similar in meaning to the word in capital letters and that rhymes with the second word.

B 5

Example CABLE tyre *wire*

26 MEAL crunch ____

27 CRAFTY fly ____

28 STRIKE clock ____

29 JAB croak ____

30 COLOUR bean ____

5

Complete the following sentences by selecting the most sensible word from each group of words given in the brackets. Underline the words selected.

B 14

Example The (children, books, foxes) carried the (houses, books, steps) home from the (greengrocer, library, factory).

31 The (girl, ship, horse) was eating (water, hay, cable) in its (stable, current, bathroom).

32 Later that (week, day, night) an owl was heard (laughing, hooting, walking) in the (distance, flowers, table).

33 Before crossing the (river, road, sky) please look both (rafts, ways, eyes) and listen for (music, traffic, clouds).

34 The (manager, major, teacher) asked his (horses, customers, pupils) to hand in their (homework, teas, umbrellas).

35 The (girls, waiters, dentists) stood in line while their (mayor, mother, mechanic) bought tickets to the (cinema, wedding, party).

5

Find and underline the two words which need to change places for each sentence to make sense. B 17

Example She went to letter the write.

36 It was too outside to play rainy.

37 The last year of the day is a Sunday.

38 January is the month first of the year.

39 Did you have lunch for your lasagne?

40 The mother was crying until her baby gave her a dummy. 5

Fill in the missing letters and numbers. The alphabet has been written out to help you. B 23

A B C D E F G H I J K L M N O P Q R S T U V W X Y Z

Example AB is to CD as PQ is to RS

41 TV is to SU as MO is to ______

42 F6 is to H8 as Q17 is to ______

43 AB is to EF as KL is to ______

44 AC is to ZX as DF is to ______

45 HJ is to QS as KM is to ______ 5

Underline the two words, one from each group, which are the most opposite in meaning. B 9

Example (dawn, early, wake) (late, stop, sunrise)

46 (quick, lazy, late) (fast, slow, busy)

47 (change, hunt, save) (spend, follow, lie)

48 (attempt, attack, attend) (hold, try, retreat)

49 (far, near, away) (distant, right, move)

50 (single, different, specific) (alone, general, unusual) 5

51–55 Write each word backwards and list them in alphabetical order. B 20

retract retreat almost enact realistic

______ ______ ______ ______ ______ 5

If the code for STILE is 36192, what are the codes for the following words? B 24

56 TIE ______

57 LIES ______

58 LIST ______ 3

If the code for RUSHES is 345725, what do the following codes stand for? B 24

59 5432 ________

60 7425 ________ 2

Ann likes sweets and toffee but not chocolate. Her sister, Jean, loves chocolate and fudge. Her friend Beata also likes chocolate and sweets, but hates fudge. Her sister Gosia likes chocolate and sweets. B 25

61 Which two items are least popular? ________

62 Which two items are most popular? ________ 2

Six children are lining up for the cinema. Mohammad is at the front and Ann is third in line. Eric does not stand next to Mohammad or Farook. Charlotte stands between Bob and Eric. Bob and Farook are not at the back of the line. B 25

63 Who is last in line? ________

64 Who is between Farook and Bob? ________

65 Who is second in line? ________ 3

Now go to the Progress Chart to record your score! **Total** 65

Paper 11

Underline the two words in each line which are most similar in type or meaning. B 5

Example	<u>dear</u>	pleasant	poor	extravagant	<u>expensive</u>
1	hungry	cheerful	sad	happy	wasteful
2	display	disappear	vanish	wonder	follow
3	flash	thunder	flare	burn	fall
4	sleep	eat	career	make	profession
5	pay	loss	deposit	consideration	salary

5

Find the three-letter word which can be added to the letters in capitals to make a new word. The new word will complete the sentence sensibly. B 22

Example The cat sprang onto the MO. USE

6 The lane was too NAR for a car. ______

7 My favourite fruit is STBERRIES. ______

8 A two-piece bathing suit is called a BII. ______

9 Do not HEATE to call if you need further advice. ______

10 I prefer NECINES to peaches. ______ 5

Find a word that can be put in front of each of the following words to make a new, compound word. B 11

Example	CAST	FALL	WARD	POUR	DOWN
11	WORK	BOAT	KEEPER	HOLD	______
12	SHELL	SHORE	SIDE	SICK	______
13	STAIRS	POUR	HILL	BEAT	______
14	STAGE	BONE	FIRE	STROKE	______
15	TOWER	DOG	WORD	MAKER	______

5

Find the four-letter word hidden at the end of one word and the beginning of the next word. The order of the letters may not be changed. B 21

Example The children had bats and balls. sand

16 She somehow managed to lose her hat every week. ______

17 The baby elephant sat down rather clumsily. ______

18 We made the decorations ourselves. ______

19 The tiny kittens lay peacefully on the rug. ______

20 My dad complained because I left the fridge door open. ______ 5

Change the first word into the last word, by changing one letter at a time and making a new, different word in the middle. B 11

Example	CASE	CASH	LASH
21	GALA	______	GATE
22	PAST	______	PORT
23	NEST	______	BENT
24	CHEW	______	BREW
25	STAR	______	SPAT

5

Find and underline the two words which need to change places for each sentence to make sense. B 17

Example She went to letter the write.

26 The radio on the music was very relaxing.

27 We finally reach to managed the bus stop.

28 His birthday was on the last month of the day.

29 The old hunting were too tired to go lions.

30 Why are we having to queue in this long wait?

Fill in the crosswords so that all the given words are included. You have been given one letter as a clue in each crossword. B 19

31

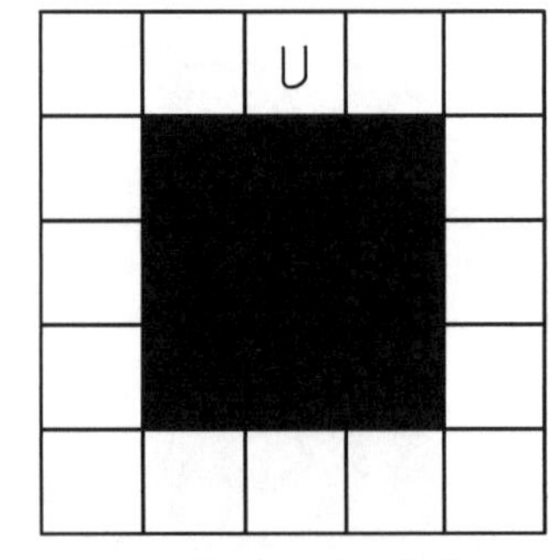

place, sleep, stunt, these

32

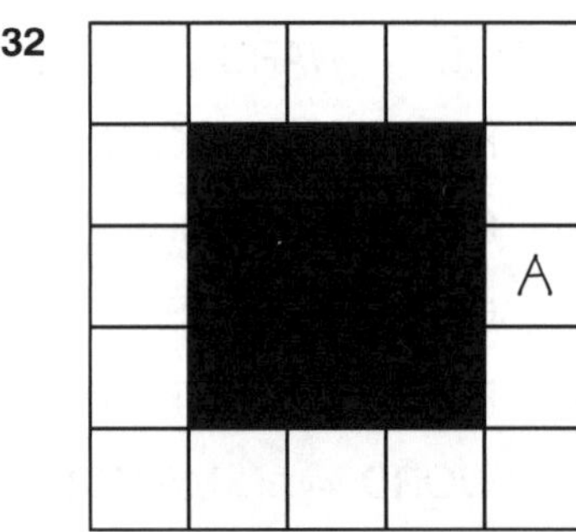

frown, names, slays, feels

33

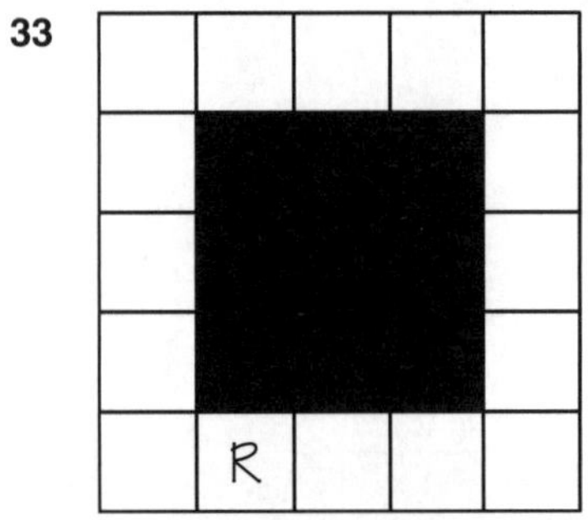

ended, freed, chose, chief

34

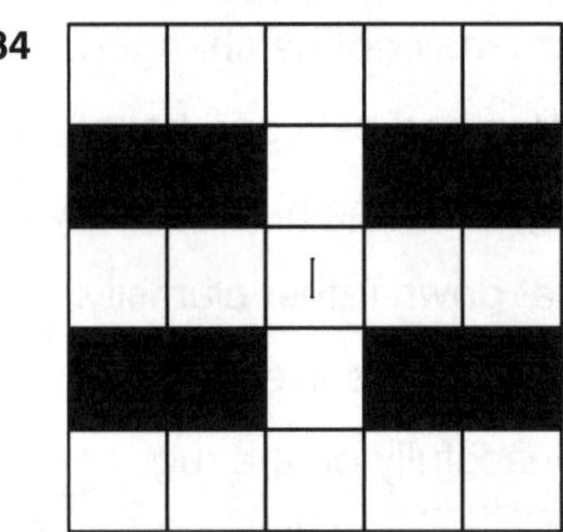

seven, prism, haste, veils

35

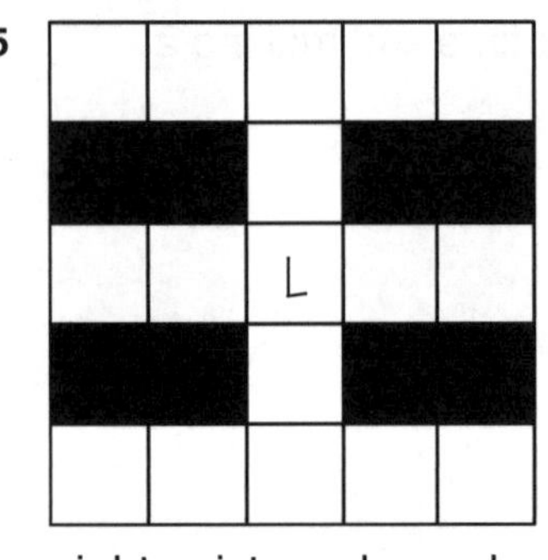

might, mists, poles, gales

5

Give the two missing pairs of letters in the following sequences. The alphabet has been written out to help you.

B 23

A B C D E F G H I J K L M N O P Q R S T U V W X Y Z

Example CQ DQ EP FP *GO* *HO*

36 AC AE AG AI ____ ____

37 CG FJ IM LP ____ ____

38 DA FC HE JG ____ ____

39 BY BW CU CS ____ ____

40 MN LO KP JQ ____ ____

5

If the code for T E A C H E R is ▲ ♥ ♦ ○ • ♥ &. What are the codes for the following words?

B 24

41 ACHE ____

42 REACH ____

43 CHEAT ____

What do these codes stand for?

44 • ♥ ♦ & ____

45 & ♦ ▲ ♥ ____

5

46–47 Read the first statement and then underline two of the five options below that must be true.

B 25

'Eagles hunt small creatures for food.'

Eagles are wild.
Eagles eat mice.
Eagles cannot see well.
People hate eagles.
Eagles are predators.

2

48–49 Read the first two statements and then underline two of the five options below that must be true.

B 25

Palm trees only grow in hot countries. Palm trees are grown in Spain.

Spain is hot.
Palm trees are found in Ireland.
Palm trees never grow in cold countries.
Spain is a city.
Palm trees grow in Antarctica.

2

50–51 Read the first two statements and then underline two of the five options below that must be true.

'Mercury and Venus are planets. They are closer to the Sun than Earth.'

Earth is hotter than Mars.

Earth is further from the Sun than Venus.

Mars is hotter than Venus.

Mercury and Earth are next to each other.

Venus is hotter than Earth.

B 25

2

Ewan, Joaquin, Alice and Gemma were discussing their favourite soap operas. Ewan and Alice are the only ones who like *Coronation Street*. Only Gemma and Alice like *Emmerdale*. Joaquin, Ewan and Gemma like *Eastenders*.

B 25

52 Which is the most popular programme? ________

53 Who likes the fewest programmes? ________

2

Rashid, Peta, Molly, Annie and Tom were discussing whether they have a computer, a television or a stereo in their bedroom. Only Peta and Annie did not have a computer. Peta only had a television. Only Rashid and Tom did not have a television. Four children had a stereo.

B 25

54 Who had a computer and television? ________

55 Who had all the same items? ________

2

If p = 2, q = 4, r = 6, s = 8, t = 10 and u = 12, give the answer to these calculations as letters.

B 26

56 $q + r$ = ________

57 $u - s$ = ________

58 $p \times q$ = ________

59 $u \div p$ = ________

60 $p \times (u - r)$ = ________

5

Solve the problems by working out the letter codes. The alphabet has been written out to help you.

B 24

A B C D E F G H I J K L M N O P Q R S T U V W X Y Z

61 In a code, FINAL is written as HKPCN. What is the code for NAIL? ________

62 In a code, BROWN is written as AQNVM. How would you write REST? ________

63 In a code, MILK is written as NJML. What does HPPE stand for? ________

64 In a code, BACK is written as ABBL. How would you write CRY? ________

65 In a code, PRESS is written as MOBPP. How would you write TOUGH? ________

5

Now go to the Progress Chart to record your score! **Total** 65

Paper 12

Underline the two words which are the odd ones out in the following groups of words.

Example black <u>king</u> purple green <u>house</u>

1	long	wide	smart	short	fast
2	head	ankle	body	leg	smile
3	oak	mud	sand	beech	elm
4	river	desert	stream	brook	ocean
5	catch	field	haul	meadow	drag

Find the three-letter word which can be added to the letters in capitals to make a new word. The new word will complete the sentence sensibly.

Example The cat sprang onto the MO. <u>USE</u>

6 Please SHAR your pencil. ______

7 The lack of rain has caused a HOSEE ban. ______

8 We do ITION and subtraction in maths. ______

9 I had to SCH my room this morning when I couldn't find my homework. ______

10 The teacher asked the pupils to take out some PR and a pen. ______

Find the letter which will complete both pairs of words, ending the first word and starting the second. The same letter must be used for both pairs of words.

Example mea (<u>t</u>) able fi (<u>t</u>) ub

11 ever (__) ellow happ (__) ule

12 faste (__) uby mise (__) oute

13 frigh (__) error spa (__) able

14 rea (__) ise pai (__) ound

15 fou (__) ight cal (__) oad

Underline two words, one from each group, that go together to form a new word. The word in the first group always comes first.

Example (hand, <u>green</u>, for) (light, <u>house</u>, sure)

16 (net, side, hat) (ball, case, mug)

17 (flat, hard, big) (room, age, mate)

18 (hit, tap, pat) (ten, tear, tern)

19 (poor, open, good) (can, door, will)

20 (car, fan, man) (ate, ear, age) 5

Find the four-letter word hidden at the end of one word and the beginning of the next word. The order of the letters may not be changed. B 21

Example The children had bats and balls. sand

21 The king finished his speech by wishing everyone goodnight. ________

22 The old man enjoyed seeing his grandchildren. ________

23 The Pope arrived back at the Vatican late that night. ________

24 They sat under the umbrella and talked until the sun went down. ________

25 Clodagh was very brave in the hospital. ________ 5

Move one letter from the first word and add it to the second word to make two new words. B 13

Example hunt sip hut snip

26 shelf sell ____ ____

27 brown shoe ____ ____

28 share mash ____ ____

29 crate pat ____ ____

30 least ton ____ ____ 5

Find and underline the two words which need to change places for each sentence to make sense. B 17

Example She went to letter the write.

31 When the wind blows the trees fall from the leaves.

32 He thought that he had come race in the first.

33 Please eat your bowl and clear away your breakfast.

34 The winner won a silver medal and the runner-up a gold one.

35 You have to find deep to dig the hidden treasure. 5

Fill in the missing letters. The alphabet has been written out to help you.

B 23

A B C D E F G H I J K L M N O P Q R S T U V W X Y Z

Example AB is to CD as PQ is to RS

36 BR is to DT as FV is to ______

37 XU is to UR as TQ is to ______

38 PN is to TJ is to SQ is to ______

39 WA is to WB is to WC is to ______

40 MN is to LO as KP is to ______

5

Here are the number codes for five words. Match the right word to the right code.

B 24

PART	PANE	NEAR	PINE	NINE
2849	2528	3528	3491	3428

41 PART ______

42 PANE ______

43 PINE ______

44 NEAR ______

45 NINE ______

5

Five children: Danny, Ella, Petra, Li and Sharif have pets. Petra has a goldfish and a hamster. Ella, Danny and Li have cats. Sharif, Li, Danny and Ella have dogs. Li does not like hamsters, but has a mouse.

B 25

46 Who has the most pets? ______

47 Which pets does Danny have? ______

48 Who only has a dog? ______

3

49 In five years' time Annabelle will be 10. How old was she three years ago? ______

B 25

50 In two years' time Jamie will be half the age of his sister, who is 12 now. How old is Jamie now? ______

2

If D = 2, F = 4, H = 6, J = 12, and L = 24, give the answers to these calculations as letters.

B 26

51 $D + D + D =$ ______

52 $J - H =$ ______

53 $D \times D =$ ______

54 $L \div J =$ ______

55 $D \times (H \div D) =$ ______

5

Change one word so that the sentence makes sense. Underline the word you are taking out and write your new word on the line. B 14

Example I waited in line to buy a book to see the film. *ticket*

56 I went to the flower station to fill up my car for the long journey. ______

57 Ellen took her sick hamster to the garage. ______

58 The cat liked to sleep near the window to catch the last of the moon's rays. ______

59 The swan stretched its graceful, long foot as it floated in the pond. ______

60 My favourite sort of ice marshmallow is chocolate. ______ 5

Solve the problems by working out the letter codes. The alphabet has been written out to help you. B 24

A B C D E F G H I J K L M N O P Q R S T U V W X Y Z

61 In a code, FASTER is written as IDVWHU. How would you write RATES? ______

62 In a code, SPORT is written as URQTV. How would you write PLUM? ______

63 In a code, MOST is written as NQVX. What does TCOI stand for? ______

64 In a code, BEAN is written as DCCL. What does UFQU stand for? ______

65 In a code, CREST is written as FUHVW. How would you write MASK? ______ 5

Now go to the Progress Chart to record your score! Total 65

Paper 13

Look at these groups of words. B 1

A	B	C	D
beef	orange	water	potato
lamb	pear	lemonade	cabbage
pork	cherry	coffee	pea

Choose the correct group for each of the words below. Write in the letter.

1 lemon ______

2 spinach ______

3 tea ______

4 chicken ______

5 grape ______ 5

Underline the two words, one from each group, which are closest in meaning. B 3

Example (race, shop, start) (finish, begin, end)

6 (old, patterned, hunt) (new, search, faint)

7 (similar, opposite, wide) (afar, last, alike)

8 (out, back, overtake) (pass, front, in)

9 (show, contain, hide) (display, cry, guess)

10 (clean, tidy, vague) (sunny, explained, unclear) 5

Underline one word in the brackets which is most opposite in meaning to the word in capitals. B 6

Example WIDE (broad vague long narrow motorway)

11 FAIL (work point pass fade call)

12 PEACE (quiet softness old calm conflict)

13 REPAIR (fix push damage flatten paint)

14 LEAD (chase trail pant follow hound)

15 CERTAIN (sure absolute positive true doubtful) 5

Underline the one word in the brackets which will go equally well with both the pairs of words outside the brackets. B 5

Example rush, attack cost, fee (price, hasten, strike, charge, money)

16 pot, tin able, willing (box, well, metal, can, agreeable)

17 delicate, weightless ignite, flare (light, heavy, hot, dim, flat)

18 smack, strike success, chart-topper (pat, stroke, winning, hit, put)

19 light, shining able, clever (fired, ablaze, bright, cunning, lively)

20 elegant, stylish hurt, ache (neat, painful, tidy, paranoid, smart) 5

Find a word that can be put in front of each of the following words to make new, compound words. B 11

Example CAST FALL WARD POUR DOWN

21 HOUSE FLY GROCER FINCH ________

22 PECKER WORM CUTTER WIND ________

23 PLACE ARM FIGHTER SIDE ________

24 BAG SHAKE RAIL WRITING ________

25 BRUSH CUT BAND DRESSER ________ 5

Find the four-letter word hidden at the end of one word and the beginning of the next word. The order of the letters may not be changed. B 21

Example The children had bats and balls. sand

26 All the boys and girls played sensibly at break-time. ________

27 Alex was ready for his grand gala centenary celebrations. ________

28 The famous actor never once forgot her lines. ________

29 After my hard work, I was glad to have scored top in my class. ________

30 I usually read for thirty minutes before I go to bed. ________ 5

Remove one letter from the word in capital letters to leave a new word. The meaning of the new word is given in the clue. B 12

Example AUNT an insect ant

31 MEAN male ________

32 STORE painful ________

33 PILOT plan ________

34 SHOP jump ________

35 TRIP tear ________ 5

Find and underline the two words which need to change places for each sentence to make sense. B 17

Example She went to letter the write.

36 We put the cake in the bake to oven.

37 We put the names in alphabetical order so Bindy came before Annabel.

38 I sometimes count on my homework when doing my maths fingers.

39 The red rose is often white or wild in colour.

40 I have red seven pages in my read level book. 5

Find the letter which will end the first word and start the second word. B 10

Example peac (h) ome

41 star (__) arth

42 cras (__) all

43 hai (__) ail

44 pac (__) ear

45 el (__) new 5

Here are the number codes for five words. Match the right word to the right code. B 24

BOOT	FALL	ALTO	TOOL	BAIL
3297	5117	3115	8277	2751

46 BOOT ______

47 FALL ______

48 ALTO ______

49 TOOL ______

50 BAIL ______ 5

Peter, David and Asif sit in a row in class. David is not beside Asif, who sits on the right of the three. B 25

51 Who sits on the left? ______

52 Who is in the middle? ______ 2

53 In six years' time Alice will be twice as old as her sister, who is two now. How old will Alice be? ______ B 25

54 Four years ago Robert was five. In five years' time he will be half the age of his brother. How old is his brother now? ______

55 Town A is south of town B, east of town D and west of town F. Town C is north-east of town A. Which town is furthest west? ______ 3

Rearrange the letters in capitals to make another word. The new word has something to do with the first two words. B 16

Example spot soil SAINT STAIN

56 twos	doubles	PARIS	______
57 goes out	leaves	EXIST	______
58 dressing	gravy	CAUSE	______
59 herb	wise	AGES	______
60 hazard	risk	GARDEN	______

5

Change one word so that the sentence makes sense. Underline the word you are taking out and write your new word on the line. B 14

Example I waited in line to buy a <u>book</u> to see the film. ticket

61 The butcher had baked several cakes. ______

62 Tame animals do not make very good pets. ______

63 The bird had constructed a beautiful hole out of twigs. ______

64 Sunday is the last month of the calendar year. ______

65 The nurse asked her pupils to take their seats. ______ 5

Now go to the Progress Chart to record your score! Total 65

Paper 14

Underline the pair of words most similar in meaning. B 5

Example	come, go	roam, wander	fear, fare
1	hurry, rest	swift, fast	break, fix
2	back, rear	hold, tie	under, over
3	polish, dirty	hunt, dog	miniature, small
4	shoot, score	aim, goal	wind, wave
5	take, give	prize, present	pole, rod

5

Underline the pair of words most opposite in meaning. B 9

Example	cup, mug	coffee, milk	hot, cold
6	wide, open	brilliant, dull	over, beyond
7	start, begin	fade, flatten	rude, polite
8	rise, fall	flake, drop	bounce, jump
9	post, join	criticise, praise	cry, wail
10	relaxed, tense	teach, instruct	lose, misplace

5

Underline the one word in the brackets which will go equally well with both the pairs of words outside the brackets. B 5

Example rush, attack cost, fee (price, hasten, strike, <u>charge</u>, money)

11 obvious, apparent fields, grassland (clear, plain, lawn, simple, ordinary)

12 elegance, beauty prayer, thanks (grace, amen, goodwill, attraction, power)

13 fill, arrange bundle, parcel (swell, gift, pack, place, pile)

14 particle, speck cereal, seed (piece, corn, bit, plant, grain)

15 sun, sky celebrity, actor (moon, star, shine, head, main) 5

Find the letter which will complete both pairs of words, ending the first word and starting the second. The same letter must be used for both pairs of words. B 10

Example mea (t) able fi (t) ub

16 star (__) ver man (__) ntry

17 car (__) angy hin (__) umble

18 sa (__) ame ho (__) rink

19 plan (__) ill hun (__) nit

20 sou (__) ale ram (__) rove 5

Find the four-letter word hidden at the end of one word and the beginning of the next word. The order of the letters may not be changed. B 21

Example The children had bats and balls. sand

21 Who let the cat in? ________

22 My dad's shed generally is rather messy. ________

23 Tremors from a severe earthquake can end up many miles away. ________

24 Fraser lent Sam a pencil because he'd left his at home. ________

25 I understand that aspirin deadens pain in the back. ________ 5

Change the first word into the last word, by changing one letter at a time and making a new, different word in the middle. B 13

Example CASE CASH LASH

26 PANT ______ PARK

27 MOST ______ MINT

28 SOUR ______ SEAR

29 BEAT ______ BRAG

30 NUTS ______ CATS 5

Look at the first group of three words. The word in the middle has been made from the other two words. Complete the second group of three words in the same way, making a new word in the middle of the group.

B 18

Example PAIN INTO TOOK ALSO SOON ONLY

31 PALE PEST STIR TAKE ______ STOP

32 SOAR OAST TIME SALE ______ ONLY

33 FOOL LOST MAST LEAP ______ STAR

34 PRICE RACE PANIC SPELT ______ BISON

35 STEAM LATE CLEAR TREND ______ CREAM

5

Find the letter which will end the first word and start the second word.

B 10

Example peac (h) ome

36 caree (__) ent

37 fir (__) dge

38 car (__) here

39 fee (__) rack

40 lam (__) atten

5

Underline the two words, one from each group, which are closest in meaning.

B 3

Example (race, shop, start) (finish, begin, end)

41 (pound, paint, wash) (beat, drop, destroy)

42 (lower, move, turn) (raise, reduce, tear)

43 (mould, attach, injure) (damage, remove, subtract)

44 (game, sickness, pattern) (repair, chess, illness)

45 (knotty, spoilt, tough) (weak, blessed, strong)

5

Find a word that can be put in front of each of the following words to make a new, compound word.

B 11

Example CAST FALL WARD POUR DOWN

46 LOCK FARE LORD PATH ______

47 FOWL FRONT LOGGED COURSE ______

48 PROOF BOARD MAN VANE ______

49 OVER BOOK PORT WORD ______

50 ACHE SPACE GROUND PACK ______

5

Fill in the missing letters and numbers. The alphabet has been written out to help you.

A B C D E F G H I J K L M N O P Q R S T U V W X Y Z

Example	CQ	DQ	EP	FP	GO	HO
51	AL	EL	IM	MM	______	______
52	AA	ZZ	BB	YY	______	______
53	ZX	XV	VT	TR	______	______
54	NM	NO	ON	OP	______	______
55	A1	C2	E3	G4	______	______

B 23

5

If ← ↑ → ↓ ↔ ϒ ↑ is the code for REPLACE, what do these codes stand for?

56 → ↑ ↔ ← ______

57 ϒ ↓ ↔ → ______

58 → ↔ ↓ ↑ ______

59 ↓ ↑ ↑ ← ______

60 → ↔ ↓ ↔ ϒ ↑ ______

B 24

5

Change one word so that the sentence makes sense. Underline the word you are taking out and write your new word on the line.

Example I waited in line to buy a book to see the film. ticket

61 Mrs Stokes found that a glass of warm milk helped her wake at night. ______

62 One of Roger's guitar notes broke as he practised. ______

63 After being fatally wounded, the soldier was pronounced alive when he reached the hospital. ______

64 Watching the moon rise is a wonderful way to start the morning. ______

65 I was so hungry because I ate all of my dinner and then had a second helping. ______

B 14

5

Now go to the Progress Chart to record your score! Total 65

Paper 15

Underline the two words, one from each group, which are closest in meaning.

B 3

Example (race, shop, start) (finish, begin, end)

1 (speak, take, ask) (request, put, give)

2 (rough, shiny, clean) (wild, glistening, dirty)

3 (destroyed, repaired, reformed) (closed, compared, broken)

4 (cross, flighty, upset) (angry, cheerful, pale)

5 (drum, stick, noise) (tap, loud, music)

5

Underline the two words, one from each group, which are the most opposite in meaning. B 9

Example (dawn, early, wake) (late, stop, sunrise)

6 (shy, old, late) (aged, confident, true)

7 (cause, result, outcome) (effect, mistake, hide)

8 (follow, collect, light) (win, heavy, succeed)

9 (tired, controlled, hungry) (starving, thirsty, energetic)

10 (numb, hurting, rare) (painful, common, protected)

5

Find the letter which will end the first word and start the second word. B 10

Example peac (h) ome

11 pai (__) ule

12 fi (__) ase

13 too (__) ast

14 cove (__) ain

15 pun (__) oung

5

Find the four-letter word hidden at the end of one word and the beginning of the next word. The order of the letters may not be changed. B 21

Example The children had bats and balls. sand

16 You are lucky as it is the final one in the shop. ______

17 He considered the cash unnecessary in the circumstances. ______

18 The Incas taught us many interesting things. ______

19 The crowd quit cheering when the team lost the ball. ______

20 He ate the bag of sweets himself. ______

5

Which one letter can be added to the front of all these words to make new words? B 12

Example care cat crate call

21 __reak __rand __all __oat

22 __oat __ool __lean __hain

23 ___ake ___orn ___oad ___urn

24 ___ir ___ate ___ind ___ault

25 ___ind ___est ___ould ___hite 5

Remove one letter from the word in capital letters to leave a new word. The meaning of the new word is given in the clue. B 12

Example AUNT an insect ant

26 DRAGOON mythical beast ____________

27 COVER bay ____________

28 ORATION limited amount ____________

29 SHINE leg ____________

30 METEOR measuring instrument ____________ 5

Find and underline the two words which need to change places for each sentence to make sense. B 17

Example She went to letter the write.

31 The old track chugged along the endless train.

32 England is one of the largest counties in Kent.

33 I really enjoy classical films and black and white music.

34 It was very home so I ran briskly late.

35 The house was delivered to the wrong newspaper by mistake. 5

Choose two words, one from each set of brackets, to complete the sentences in the best way. B 15

Example Tall is to (tree, short, colour) as narrow is to (thin, white, wide).

36 Speedy is to (fast, slow, late) as low is to (last, high, calm).

37 Ignore is to (overlook, welcome, accept) as praise is to (forget, change, honour).

38 Well is to (water, ill, better) as mine is to (wood, coal, wheat).

39 Damp is to (wet, sandy, dry) as cool is to (snow, rain, cold).

40 Kite is to (fly, sky, bird) as badger is to (nest, zoo, mammal). 5

If A = 1, B = 4, D = 5, E = 10, S = 20, what are the sums of the following words by adding the letters together? B 26

41 BAD = ______

42 SEED = ______

Give the answer to these calculations as letters.

43 S – E = ______

44 (A + B) + D = ______

45 E – D = ______

5

Find the letter which will complete both pairs of words, ending the first word and starting the second. The same letter must be used for both pairs of words. B 10

Example mea (t) able fi (t) ub

46 clai (__) ost cal (__) en

47 pra (__) olk tr (__) oung

48 pac (__) nd craz (__) ase

49 bal (__) ose foo (__) eck

50 ful (__) oot scraw (__) and

5

Rearrange the letters in capitals to make another word. The new word has something to do with the first two words. B 16

Example spot soil SAINT STAIN

51	jump	hop	PALE	______
52	untrue	unreal	FLEAS	______
53	not strong	fragile	WAKE	______
54	annoys	upsets	RANGES	______
55	fruit	canteloupe	LEMON	______

5

Change the first word into the last word, by changing one letter at a time and making a new, different word in the middle. B 13

Example CASE CASH LASH

56 POST ______ PACT

57 MICE ______ MATE

58 ARTS ______ AIMS

59 SHIP ______ SNAP

60 FLOW ______ FLAT

5

Fill in the missing letters and numbers. The alphabet has been written out to help you. B 23

A B C D E F G H I J K L M N O P Q R S T U V W X Y Z

Example AB is to CD as PQ is to RS

61 DN is to BL as GQ is to ______

62 BB is to YY as DD is to ______

63 JJ is to LM as QQ is to ______

64 ZY is to ZX as ZW is to ______

65 A1 is to B2 as Y25 is to ______ 5

Now go to the Progress Chart to record your score! **Total** 65

Progress Chart Verbal Reasoning 9-10 years Book 2

Total marks	Paper 1	2	3	4	5	6	7	8	9	10	11	12	13	14	15	Percentage
65																100%
60																90%
55																85%
																80%
50																
45																70%
40																60%
35																
																50%
30																
25																40%
20																30%
15																
																20%
10																
5																10%
0																0%
	1	2	3	4	5	6	7	8	9	10	11	12	13	14	15	
Date																

When you've finished the book use the Next Steps Planner